How to Heal and Be Healed
A Guide to Health in Times of Change

Paul Lambillion

Gateway

Gateway
an imprint of
Gill & Macmillan Ltd
Hume Avenue
Park West
Dublin 12
with associated companies throughout the world
www.gillmacmillan.ie

© 2002 Paul Lambillion
0 7171 3415 6
Illustrations adapted by Alanna Corballis
from the author's originals
Index compiled by Susan Williams
Print origination by Carole Lynch, Dublin
Printed by ColourBooks Ltd, Dublin

*The paper used in this book is made from the wood pulp
of managed forests. For every tree felled, at least one tree
is planted, thereby renewing natural resources.*

A catalogue record is available for this book
from the British Library.

1 3 5 4 2

Dedication

To Sue, Ruth, Dominic, John and Megan
and to all those aware of their own healing journeys.

My love and thanks.

Paul

CONTENTS

finding the centre - Exercise 5
p.61

Contents

INTRODUCTION

Sometime in the mid 1980s, I wrote to the head office of a well-known High Street chemist, one with branches in most towns in the UK, enquiring why it was that they didn't stock natural remedies, particularly homoeopathic and essence medicines.

The terse reply I received suggested that such medicines were pharmaceutically unproven and that the chemist sold only tried and tested drugs and treatments which were part of the more orthodox, chemically based repertoire.

Somewhere along the way, there has obviously been a massive change of heart, for the same company now gives a very high profile on its shelves to the natural medicines it once dismissed out of hand. The reason for this one can only surmise, but no doubt the changes in the public perception as to what healing and health may be, and the economic significance of such a shift, have had their impact.

I have been actively involved in complementary medicine for twenty years, for much of that time professionally, and it has long since been my view that no individual or medicine has actually healed anyone. It has become clear to me that healing is an inner, personal process which others can help and encourage, and some medicines may assist, but it is ultimately governed by a higher, more profound unique intelligence within the individual. If this were not true, we would all respond to the same therapeutic and pharmaceutical ministrations in the same way, and disease control would be a relatively simple, logical and structured process. The appropriate magic bullet would work for everyone, which is now increasingly seen as not the case. Disease is more complex than that.

Furthermore, as soon as we overcome one strand of disease, we find ourselves seeking the cure for a new one, or a mutation of an old scourge. In my childhood, the fears still centred on such things as TB, poliomyelitis, and childhood leukemia. Venereal diseases were also still wreaking havoc, although penicillin was beginning to work its magic as a panacea for all infections — an illusion already breaking down as resistant strains of bacteria evolve.

As well as the physical dimension, we face a continuing growth in emotional illness. Psychoactive drugs and the demand for them grows exponentially, both the prescribed and pro-scribed varieties. Tranquillizer addiction has become a disease in its own right, and Prozac was briefly viewed as a 'designer drug' by some, a necessary crutch when dealing with a busy, frantic, yet empty, materialistic life and its vacillating fortunes.

Then there are the energy diseases, conditions for which there is often no pathological framework to explain them. They are many — ME, fatigue, exhaustion, depression, post-viral syn-drome, SAD and so on. The increasing incidence of these and other problems is particularly challenging since there appears to be no specific treatment structure for them, persisting some-times, as they can, for years and years, affecting young and old.

But this picture is hardly surprising. In our modern society, we eat junk food, we fill our minds with junk television or computer games. We live life at a ridiculous, hectic pace, rarely nurturing ourselves properly.

We spend hours on computers communicating with strangers, but don't know who our neighbours are and we surround our-selves with a mass of electrical gadgetry, pouring out an increas-ingly powerful cocktail of wave phenomena which, we are told by experts, is harmless to us, or, at least, within 'safe limits'.

In my work, I have observed the effects of this modern life, and this book is based upon that experience and the approaches

I have found effective in the quest for healing. These approaches have more in common with the natural medicines and their subtle, energetic influences, once ignored by our aforementioned High Street retailers, than with much contemporary orthodox practice.

We are in unique times: fast changing, difficult, yet, I believe, potentially wonderful times. We are changing, as are our perceptions of illness and disease, and the disease is changing with us.

Our methods of healing are increasingly based upon a very old model of ourselves, destroyed by Descartian thinking, now re-asserting itself as people search to find real answers, rather than quick fixes. An image of Man, now re-emerging in the public psyche, shows him not simply as a physical creature with some kind of mental faculty, but as a complex, intricate being — an entity of many layers, all of which must be involved and considered if true healing is to take place. This is the wholistic way.

This book is written from such a viewpoint.

It is a workbook for those who seek to be healed — body, mind, emotion and spirit — those who wish to be whole and take control as much as they may, for their own health and healing. It is also for those who seek to help others.

I am not suggesting a sudden forsaking of conventional practice, as that would be foolish, and everything has its time and its place. But to experience deep, permanent healing, those of us alive today must search beyond the boundaries of current orthodoxy and draw upon the wonderful resources with which we are all magically endowed.

Paul Lambillion
Bury St Edmunds, 2002

CHAPTER 1

A RELUCTANT HEALER —
A BACKGROUND

It had never really entered my mind, consciously at least, that I should be anything remotely like a carer or therapist. After some occasional successes as a singer, I had assumed that my working life would probably be something rather conventional. My life-long, if largely secret, vision of auras, energies and the 'invisible' worlds provided me with interesting, if puzzling, insights, but I had no idea that they held the key to my future work. If anything, I was rather afraid of it. I flirted briefly with the possibility of becoming a priest, but apart from the unattractiveness a life of celibacy held for me, there were inner currents of restlessness that would have made me quite an unsuitable candidate. The spiritual life enthralled me, even when I briefly deserted it, but I could never show unquestioning loyalty and obedience to dogma and not think freely for myself. I'm sure I would have incurred the wrath of my seniors sooner rather than later if I had followed the ecclesiastical path.

Communication skills I had. 'A born teacher' was how I was described by a tutor on my teaching course. And so, that was the course I eventually followed.

With the inevitable benefits of hindsight, I can now see how I seemed to have the ability to develop good relationships with some of the more troubled and troublesome pupils. The rogues seemed to trust me, perhaps sensing something of their own unruliness in their teacher. I have since discovered that my disciplined approach was seen by most of my pupils to be fair and caring, and even the most uncooperative of youngsters would usually respond eventually to my methods and sincerity.

However, as is often the case with those involved in therapeutics, it was as a consequence of difficulties of my own that my quest for healing commenced, leading ultimately to my helping thousands of others to find their own healing too.

Collapse

During the early 1970s, whilst developing a very successful teaching career — I was a rapidly rising star — I began to experience some problems. Over a period of several days, I had noticed how I was becoming more and more sensitive. My familiar bouncy energy had given way to an increasing lethargy and I felt tired most of the time.

One fateful day, while working an absolutely ridiculous schedule, with no balance between activity and rest, I experienced collapse. Crawling into school, feeling most unwell, I conducted an interview for a new assistant in my department. Whilst showing the successful candidate around afterwards, I became breathless, faint, overwhelmed by a terrible feeling of doom, and I thought I was having a heart attack. The auras I had always seen glowed with an astounding intensity and clarity, seeming so much more real than the people and objects to which they were attached. It was a terrifying experience, close in some respects to when I had been struck by lightning in my teens. I felt close to death.

The consequences were enormous. I was no longer the same energetic, lively individual I had been, and it would be many years before I would again become that person.

Medical tests revealed nothing significant, so exhaustion was diagnosed and rest prescribed, which meant taking nearly two months off work. I desperately wanted to return and to be who I used to be. But I couldn't, and I simply did not understand what had happened to me. Words like 'breakdown' were freely bandied about, but, strangely enough, my mind was fairly sound during this period. However, I didn't feel right — I could not retain energy for very long, and every little exercise required rest afterwards.

Another bizarre effect was that, along with an intensification of my vision of auras and energy fields, I found atmospheres and crowds of people sometimes impossible to tolerate. Rooms would affect my equilibrium and physical balance — like a bat whose radar was over re-active — and the thoughts and feelings of others sometimes struck me like knives hitting a weak, soft target. Often my poor wife would have to accompany me as I made a sudden abrupt departure from a room, or pub, because the feelings there overwhelmed me, quite unexpectedly. 'Claustrophobia' it was called. Over-sensitivity to subtle forces — both energetic (electromagnetic) mental and emotional forces — is what it was.

Later, I will explore these forces and these situations and the important reality they reveal — and also the routes to healing we can follow as we encounter them.

The Healing Man

My body continued to be wracked with pain; my vitality was as unpredictable and variable as the proverbial yo-yo; my confidence had only slightly returned.

Tranquillizing drugs offered no real help — in the long term they made things worse. So a friend suggested that I go to see a special man who could do unusual things to help people. This man, I later discovered, was a healer, someone with a supernormal ability to help others, sometimes healing them, but at least, through the laying on of hands, bringing some easement into their minds and bodies. Desperation brings with it a willingness to try anything, and, in desperation, I visited this man in a small room attached to a house in Westcliff-on-Sea, Essex.

First view showed an ordinary man, a piano tuner by trade. I waited in his little room, feeling strangely calm in a situation where one would normally be a little anxious.

I was beckoned to sit closer to him and, without any input from me, he was able to discuss my condition with me, giving a complete and accurate diagnosis of all the symptoms I had experienced. I initially suspected some collusion between my friend Norman who had introduced me, and this healer. However, with a little reflection, I was very sure that it had not been so — Norman was a person of the highest integrity whom I respected totally and he assured me that he had told the healer nothing. And he had nothing to gain from such deception.

When he laid his hands on me, the healer did so with a gentleness bordering on tenderness and I could see the remarkable movements of energy and coloured light through his body and also around my own. And although I had witnessed such things on countless occasions, this was a particularly spectacular display. Having left me wrapped in a cloak of beautiful and very peaceful energy, the session concluded. I was told I could leave and, as I stood to do so, the healer smiled. His countenance changed and so too did his voice. Then came the words that were to prove so important for me, although it was to be some years before I would understand their true significance and, indeed, that of the whole experience. 'One day you will heal others. It is your Karma. You are able to see the signs.'

He said nothing else to me. And I departed, a little puzzled and yet with an optimism and calmness I hadn't experienced for many weeks. Stepping out into the May sunlight, I found everything brighter, clearer and more powerful. My vision of subtle forces had been heightened and everyone and everything glowed in swathes of wonderful light. I didn't realise at the time that a long healing journey had begun and I would receive that message several times more over the next few years, from different people, in different places, before I took the necessary steps to unearth whatever it was that I was meant to do. But I just couldn't envisage myself as a healer at that time. The reluctance I felt was not an unwillingness to help others. It was more a disbelief that I was an individual of sufficient virtue or ability to work in such a wonderful way.

As the years went by, through various trials and difficulties, I began to manage myself better. There were still to be significant problems and many moments of despair. But a fire had been lit, and such ignition is never dampened down — not in me or anyone else.

Feelings and Visions

There is often a connection between powerful, active imagination, poor sleep, hypersensitivity, anxiety states and migraine. Children, and indeed adults, who experience erratic sleep patterns often have minds that are not focused, trying to process too many ideas at one time.

I had many periods where the visions and images that drifted through my mind were impacting upon me with excessive force and rapid frequency. On bad days, an atmosphere could almost rip me apart. The feelings I had encountered since childhood surfaced with even greater intensity, often not abating for days, whereas previously such feelings had dissipated in minutes. I felt that life was punishing me, but for what I did not know.

The realisation began to dawn on me that what I could see and sense might be indicative of a gift, or an ability of some kind, which, when properly harnessed, might be useful in some way. But it was still a problem for me which I had to learn to manage and understand. I felt that no amount of therapy or medication would do for me what I had to do for myself. Such things would help, but it was really about taking charge again, and I had to find out how.

Since a small boy, I had recognised the value of prayer, stillness, and the quiet — the marvellous, beautiful aura of light that explodes around those who touch their deep inner peace. I decided to research and learn to meditate, to relax and to study the science of breath. This involved some false starts, many teachers — some enlightened, some not so. They all taught me something, but mostly I learned empirically, using myself as the laboratory, the testing ground.

Breathing Through

The first thing I did was to learn to manage my breathing, and I studied the various techniques associated with yoga and pranic breathing. It was not totally alien to me as I had studied singing for years and the matter of diaphragmatic control is central to any good singing. I discovered how the breath would calm down my system as it experienced difficulties and, gradually, increase my strength and power thresholds.

I learned to breathe myself through crisis and panic, through the cold turkey of tranquillizer withdrawal, although in the early days it was not without its moments of comedy. Crossing Victoria Station one day, the atmosphere and hustle and bustle, the vibrations and noises came crashing in upon me. The auras of individuals pulsed with a remarkable, yet increasingly intimidating dynamism as they scurried to and fro across the massive concourse linking the many platforms. The energy of the place bore down heavily and I quickly linked to my rhythmic breathing as I walked manfully towards the ticket office. The depth of the energising breath kept the panic at bay, although when my turn came to be at the front of the queue, I had to adopt a rather stilted, robotic speech — words snatched between controlling breaths. The poor ticket clerk was bemused at my conversational style — I must have sounded like an alien visiting from another planet.

However, I was triumphant. It was early days, but I was learning all over again to manage my response to people and atmospheres. I remember boarding the train for Margate, in Kent, my smile a hundred yards wide, my solar plexus gently glowing, my head clear and the energies around me looking bright, powerful, a little frantic, but no longer menacing. I was on my way.

A Deepening Consciousness

In the late 1970s I had been receiving mantra meditation instruction from a very sweet and kind woman who had been involved in the TM movement of the Maharishi. She had good experience and I developed a trust in her. She too had overcome many personal difficulties, including the mysterious disappearance of her husband whilst on a flight that had gone missing over the Bermuda Triangle many years before. The wreckage of the plane was never discovered, nor were any bodies found. She had a simple radiance, her aura was very clear and open and she was herself a notably perceptive individual.

As one who had prayed and reflected all my life — a positive consequence of my Catholic childhood — I took to meditational practices like the proverbial duck to water. During the learning process, my body gradually became cleared of heaviness, just as mud washes from a car when exposed to jets of fine, warm water. I could now feel the energy coursing through the channels of my body, and the light of my own aura became discernible with increasing clarity.

Perhaps more significantly, I could observe, in a controlled manner, the energy movements in others, including my fellow students, watching the healing taking place especially in those who were serious and diligent in following the meditation practices they had been taught. It became apparent that the dedicated were embarking upon a remarkable journey of self-healing and that they would never be the same again.

It proved to be an enormous turning point for me. One or two fellow students would openly discuss these processes of change with me, one dear lady even commenting on the healing surge she felt at those times.

'You must be a healer,' she said. 'I can feel it when I talk with you.'

'No,' I replied. 'I am not a healer. You are the healer; indeed, we all are.' And although I have never liked the term *healer*, I have gradually learned what that statement meant as it impacted upon me so profoundly.

We hear many things in our chatter-filled lives. Most of them wash through us, barely noticed, often hardly registering. 'You hear what you want to hear' is a common charge made against us when we fail to acknowledge or recall the words aimed in our direction. I see it as another aspect of an unfocused, throw-away society, where everything is dispensable or disposable, including our words — more flotsam to be disregarded as our mood takes us, both when delivered and when received.

However, some words really strike us with a meaningful, deadly accuracy. I was to learn just how much words matter as this phrase was echoed over and over again. I wasn't sure that I wanted to hear it, but I couldn't ignore it either.

Thoughts and Fields of Power

I studied meditation from many traditions and with several teachers. My innate laziness sometimes slowed progress, but a deeper, more urgent desire to know and to learn more always surfaced to push along my studies, and I began to feel better with each passing day.

One teacher observed how I used to 'disappear' during meditation. He had never seen it before and didn't know what to make of it. 'You appear to leave the room and become invisible,' he remarked. 'What happens to you? Where do you go?'

I was unable to answer his question. In fact, it is only recently, working with a client with a history of health problems and unusual experiences, that I have witnessed the same phenomenon. What was significant was the integration that took place in my awareness during his sessions. I was always grateful that his simple approach helped to clarify the meaning behind so many things I saw and felt, and longed to understand. Another intelligence stirred and it was calibrating my mind in a more ordered, structured fashion.

Now I could see not only the effects of thoughts upon the physical body, but also how our emotional patterns could disrupt our energy and vitality, sometimes profoundly and with concomitant danger to health. During this period I also learned that people do not so much have 'blocks', but rather excessive or constricted flows of energy and power through their personal energy fields and subtle bodies of the aura.

It also became clearer to me how we could be affected by the various waves and radiations around us — both those man-made ones and those occurring spontaneously in our environment.

I remember watching a very tall, thin, pale man one day as he walked by the window of an electrical shop. The window was full of active televisions, their screens blazing into the street beyond. As he passed by, his energy fields palpably changed. The normally beautiful clear-coloured light of his mental and emotional auras changed to reveal transient swathes of flux in nearly all the colours visible, as if they had been exposed to strong gusts of some strange wind. Watching more intently, I observed a bending and twisting motion in his energy body that would have had a temporary depleting effect on his vitality, and would have tired him. Once he had passed, his aura seemed to recover and return to a more balanced state. Further observations confirmed that the same thing happened to everyone who crossed the path of the radiations, sometimes more profoundly, sometimes a little less so, but the effects were clear to see and were constant. It would be a while before I would fully appreciate the significance of this and other observations and the ramifications for human health — mental and emotional, as well as physical. To be exposed to such things continually is certainly a risk to our health.

As my own healing unfolded, my inner awareness was growing, and consequently my subtle perception of others was becoming more reliable, more penetrating and more revealing.

X-Ray Vision

I decided to test my own ability as a healer, working briefly with a local group of fine, sincere people. Whilst my tuition was virtually non-existent — I was told I was 'a natural', whatever that may mean — I watched what other healers did and basically copied them. I always thought it was a little like the therapeutic equivalent of learning to dance — observe the steps of others and do likewise!

Many things happened but I particularly recall the development of what my giggling friends referred to as X-ray vision. Today in my work I encounter many individuals who have a similar experience. It is surprisingly common in the development of energy healers and therapists of all disciplines and traditions; clients often tell me they can see 'blocks' or organ problems in the physical bodies of others. This has both its constructive and perilous sides, as you can no doubt imagine, and such ability in the hands of a novice can cause more problems than it might solve.

Suffice to say that, as I worked with a steady stream of patients, I found myself able to tune into an organ or area of physical tissue and often see it with a remarkable clarity. Whilst I have always used this vision with caution and very seldom utilise it now as there are more efficient ways and more appropriate methods of analysis which can be made through the energy field, it has none the less proved useful on occasion.

The Healthy Kidney

One early case given to me to learn from (all healers and indeed therapists learn from their patients — failure to acknowledge this is foolish and hinders the practitioner's development) was that of a young woman who had a tumour diagnosed on one kidney. Further investigation was planned, along with the removal of the offending tumour and the organ to which it was attached. When she came to me, shortly after the diagnosis, I looked at her aura as I made my preliminary notes and I felt that the information being given to me in the colours did not suggest morbid or cancerous tissue. However, as is best in such cases, I said nothing, but looked again, this time accessing a little picture of each kidney in her body. I could see nothing other than two healthy kidneys, functioning reasonably well. There may have been an infection of some kind but it had obviously cleared.

After the healing session had concluded, I confirmed with the patient that she was to have a further examination before any surgery or other treatment would be commenced. She looked at me with a puzzled expression across her face. 'Why do you ask?' she enquired.

I kept my counsel, vaguely suggesting that it would perhaps be a good idea, simply to make sure that things were as they had appeared to be. A little while later, after further tests, the woman returned. Her smile was broad and she was full of bounce and vitality. Further X-rays and examinations had revealed that no tumour or unusual tissue was present, and the physician felt that something had been amiss in the earlier diagnosis.

At first, she wanted to thank me for removing the tumour. However, I was able to confide in her now that I had felt all along that there was no problem.

The Grapefruit Tumour

Mary was in late middle age. She was listless and her life seemed devoid of direction and purpose. She hoped that a reading of her aura and some healing energy would put her in touch with her life's pattern.

Within a few moments of our meeting, my vision was drawn to her abdomen and the particular rays of light visible in the aura around that area of her body. Immediately and spontaneously, my vision switched to view her inner organs, and an unpleasant-looking physical mass was visible, nestling on her bowel. I had to keep our thoughts away from fear and negativity, for tumours thrive on the energy generated by negative mental activity, so I enquired a little more generally into her health. She confessed to having 'gone off' her food and also to experiencing some abdominal discomfort, especially a while after eating a substantial meal.

I suggested that perhaps a check up by her GP might be useful. I was always cautious that perhaps my vision might have been wrong, and to frighten her unnecessarily would have been very irresponsible and counter-productive, and would have created the very conditions I was trying to help her remove. Within days, she was admitted to hospital, and a tumour 'the size of a grapefruit' was removed from her body.

I learned much from this experience, not the least of which was the responsibility such vision places upon the beholder, and also how a tactful, constructive approach is needed. In the wrong hands such gifts can be dangerous.

Intelligent Energy

As a healer's reputation develops, many tests come along to refine and unfold their capacity and effectiveness. Josie's energy field was always very vibrant and visible. She was the friend and colleague of a neighbour who nursed at the local hospital. Josie was attached to our local health centre as a chiropodist and was an effervescent, bouncy, young Ugandan of Asian descent.

By this time, I was accustomed to watching the energy flows in people, trying to understand them more and to understand what they told me. Josie's were like a beacon of clarity. A pretty girl, she had some cystic growths on her face, which, whilst not in any sense a real health risk, were unsightly. Treatment consisted solely of surgical removal, with the attendant scarring that she wished to avoid.

Josie knew of my interest and work in healing and had visited a 'witch doctor' previously in Uganda. At the time, being linked to such strange traditions compounded my continuing unease at being viewed a healer, although my natural desire to help others was gradually eliminating some of the embarrassment I felt. Such feelings stem from an acquired sense of unworthiness common to us all. Josie felt that I might be able to help her a little regarding her cysts, and she arrived one evening for a session.

By this time, I had begun to work with individuals on their own self-healing process, using meditation and exercises specifically geared to my observations of their aura and subtle energy system. I felt more comfortable when helping individuals to take responsibility for themselves, increasingly seeing myself as an enabler.

As I guided Josie through a brief energy-clearing exercise, I watched the strands of energy and light moving between the major and secondary energy centres, or chakra vortices, and saw some noticeable constrictions in her lumbar region. However, Josie had mentioned no other problem and, when I attuned to healing energy with my hands, I concentrated my attention purely upon her head as she had asked me to do, placing my hands in that part of her aura.

Some three days later, she called me. 'What did you do to my back?' Her tone of voice revealed considerable bewilderment. 'I was in agony when I left you, but now it's cleared and my lower back is pain-free again. It's the best it's been in years.'

Her determined pursuit of a remedy for her facial and largely cosmetic problem had led Josie to neglect to tell me of her long-term back injury, sustained when working on a market in Kampala as a teenager. I had briefly spotted the energy constriction but had not touched her lower spine at all. However, the human energy flow is wonderfully intelligent and it knew what to do and where the priority for her was to be found. A healed back is more important than a slight facial nuisance and the clever energy knew that and behaved accordingly, whatever she and I decided.

Wheels of Fire

'She is angry with everybody,' her father said, obviously distressed at his young daughter's depression and her recent bizarre and uncharacteristic behaviour that had led to her exclusion from school and to fights with some of her schoolmates. 'We've tried everyone and you're our last hope.'

I would often hear words like those and how they still perturbed me, resurrecting my lingering feelings of inadequacy. Increasingly, the desperate came to see me, and my learning curve was sharp and daunting. But my reluctance was gently being modified by my growing vision and appreciation of the hidden power and creativity in all people, even those in extreme poor health and difficult situations. I knew that I didn't have to heal them — in fact, I couldn't; no one could. But I could help them to heal themselves.

The wheels of fire — the chakras in her aura — spun and turned very visibly, some uncontrollably quickly, others slowly and sluggishly. The normally glistening light around the heart was disturbed and erratic, yet, just below it, her solar plexus limped round in a turgid, uneven, sluggish rotation. Her heart chakra showed that she was confused, unable to deal with the demands of many friendships in the volatile time of adolescence — no longer child but not yet woman. Her solar plexus was depressed. She was exhausted, trying to cope with her rapidly changing nature and the poor self-image that was currently dominant in her mind. She was afraid and unhappy with who she was and even more apprehensive of who she might become.

'Don't be hard on yourself,' I said to her. 'I think you have much to give.' She lifted her eyes and gave me a tense, yet hopeful, glance. The light in her solar plexus immediately brightened for a while, its rotational movement quickening slightly for a few moments. Here was hope visible. Many conversations, meditations and healing exercises, including forgiveness, followed our first meeting. Her heart stopped racing, her solar plexus quickened, her confidence returned and she glowed once more, able to return to school and her studies more confident and more at ease. She stopped being so afraid and disappointed with herself and began to rise up like a phoenix from the ashes of despair. Her parents were amazed at how much she had changed.

The Web of Light

I could now understand the messages from the subtle forces and light of the aura, and how we can work with our deeper natures to bring healing into ourselves and the lives of others. The splendour of the light and reserves of power in even the most sick and troubled of individuals never ceased to astound me. Even when we are ill, so much of us is still well.

One day, I sat in my small garden, enjoying a few minutes' reverie. It was a lovely, sun-soaked evening. I focused on the lilac bush in the corner — the energy and aura around it were always quite remarkable. In a moment, my mind suddenly lifted back into the garden of my early childhood, with the lilac tree nestling close to the little summerhouse we had there. The present moment blurred and merged with the warm memories from the past, and the wonderful world of light from those days dominated my awareness — a world dancing with colours, streams of light, fairies, angels and every strand of the subtle magic we know in our childhood, but leave behind in our dash into adulthood. It is a world we forget, yet still yearn for, as we grow older.

I saw how the tree exchanged vitality with the earth's field around it — a vast ocean of rhythms and waves, of differentiated forces and their energies, a web of consciousness in which everything can gain expression, grow and thrive. Happy tears filled my eyes. I became more and more deeply immersed in the sheer beauty and incredible potential of what I saw and felt at that moment.

Everything was seeking to support everything else — the potential for healing was truly unlimited. It was for us to acknowledge it, tap into it and allow it to work in us.

As a very little boy, I would sit in the cinema with my parents and older sister. The emotional energy and dramatic setting of the movie would take my mind away from the cinema to the thoughts and powerful feelings we all encounter in those peak moments when a deep sense of destiny touches us, albeit briefly.

'What should I be? — I have to do something special, something needed by life. I have to change the world — be a doctor or politician — I have to make a difference for people.' I really had those thoughts, often, as John Wayne won the West or the goodies beat the baddies in the eternal metaphor for good defeating evil. My work would lead me to understand that most, if not all, of us have such visions, such aspirations in our childhood. Through the ups and downs, the little boy with strange visions became the not-so-reluctant healer and helper.

I have learned largely through observing, testing and deduction. There have been few official teachers, but many who have guided and allowed me into their lives, to learn what I needed to learn. One renowned spiritual teacher once said to me, 'Your job is to help people sort themselves out.'

With hindsight, he was absolutely right.

CHAPTER 2

EASE AND DIS-EASE

The Human Spirit has its source in the Divine Fountain, which must be permitted to flow freely, through man. Anyone who flows as life flows, has solved the enigma of human existence. This person needs no other power. Everything is healthy which flows with the Universe.

Lao Tzu

He had been clear of cancer for some time, and recent tests had revealed a very healthy picture. His whole family was delighted, as was I. The healing package, conventional and holistic, had returned him to his former bounce and confidence, and the future looked bright.

I could not see a trace of morbidity in his body. Then his elderly mother, to whom he was extremely close — perhaps closer than to anybody — became unwell. There was no special diagnosis — she was simply worn out after a long, busy, hard-working life. And when, after a few days, she was removed to hospital, most of the family sensed that she was about to make her transition from this life to the next. She had the peaceful calmness that comes with our resignation to the inevitable, as our soul takes control and we are prepared to move on. The light around her clearly indicated that, and the crown chakra at the top of her head became bright and extremely dynamic and active, streams of light flowing wonderfully in and out of her aura.

For her, it was quite a wonderful time. For her son, it wasn't. He couldn't and wouldn't let go of her, and her passing drained him deeply. His vitality seemed to ebb away; the spark went and he was no longer at ease with life. It seemed to hold no interest for him despite his being a young man, and he became like an alien on a strange planet.

In the period immediately after his mother's passing, the common emotional constraints we experience at such a time — most prevalent in the solar plexus — instead of loosening and being released through the grief process, became more and more intense, and he began to experience pain in his stomach and his side. An initial test showed nothing abnormal but, as the symptoms persisted, a later examination revealed liver cancer.

Shortly afterwards, he died. I have never seen anyone go from ease to dis-ease so quickly and so dramatically. The flow of power in him became strangled and ultimately severed as the will to live evaporated.

Health, or wholeness — that state of ease where life's magic and forces flow through us — is an active process. We have to allow or enable ourselves to be well, at ease, or at least as well as we can be. Disease is exactly what it says — a constriction of the flow of life's forces as they percolate down from the soul or our highest spiritual nature, through to our personality self, from the universal to the human. To be well, we have to be in the centre of this flow, as we are intended always to be, allowing life to pour through us, continually, as much as it can.

The Human Subtle Anatomy

Perhaps before I go further, I should define the model of the human being and its mechanism with which I work in my practice and which I refer to throughout this book. It is not complete — it cannot be — but it is a useful model based upon my vision and experience.

Our physical body is one aspect of our personality — the heaviest, densest aspect of our human, planetary self. It is a wonderful construct, containing remarkable complex interwoven systems of organs and tissue, allowing our experience on the earth here to unfold. Through it we see, hear, touch, smell and taste life and we are able to celebrate our three-dimensional nature through our creativity as we seek to find and fulfil our purpose.

This complex mass, however, is both supported by and dependent upon many other layers, within both our personality and also our higher nature or soul.

Figure 2.1: The personality bodies

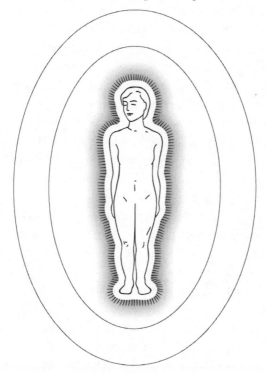

The Etheric or Energy Self

The energy body interacts directly with the physical body, and they are essentially two aspects of one and the same plane (cf. Lambillion, *Auras and Colours*, Gateway, 2001) This body is sometimes given other names: etheric body or double vitality body, elemental body, or bioplasmic or pranic body.

This body enables us to exist in the energy or etheric plane of the earth, which in turn exists in the energy or etheric plane of the sun. The sun and its energy body are a part of the universal etheric or energy plane. We are in a continuous state of exchange with the etheric plane and its power, via our etheric or energy body. We absorb and process energy, returning it back to its plane or field around us.

The notion of an all-embracing field of energy, ether or aether, was a commonly held scientific and medical idea up until the twentieth century when it was abandoned. Mystics have seen it for generations. It is the basis of much yoga, and of practices such as tai chi and feng shui, and it is regaining ground through the work of such scientists as Fritjof Capra, Rupert Sheldrake and others who now consider this field a reality.

The CIA and the KGB of the former Soviet Union have also spent vast budgets, exploring the nature of this field and its relationship to the human mind, as documents now released by the Defense Agency in the USA show.

This field is the intelligence and power behind our physical natures, acting on one level like a pattern or matrix for the physical structure of the body. Where there is a physical heart, there is an energy heart; where there is a physical brain, there is an energy or etheric counterpart, and so on, all the way through the physical body.

The energetic aspect keeps the physical organ in place, and allows it to continue in its process of continuous rebuilding and renewal in line with the master pattern imprinted in the energy body, the official blue-print, it could be said. In disease, this process has broken down, either temporarily or permanently, and the organ or tissue is no longer rebuilding itself as it should. In effect, a breakdown in communication ensues.

An earlier book of mine mentioned how this creates a problem in organ transplantation surgery, for each cell and each organ resonates at a unique frequency. Every human organ is different in vibration from every other, both of other types and of the same kind. So, the implantation of a donated organ into a physical body creates a dissonance between it and its energy blueprint. Anti-rejection drugs can numb this down a little, and in the short term it is a valuable approach, but it is not the way forward in the longer term. I am sure that, in time, we will learn how to re-grow organs and tissues in perfect harmony with the etheric template upon which they are formed. After all, under an electron microscope, our whole physical nature is reduced down to a mass of electrical activity, held together in differing patterns of manifestation by some elusive intelligence.

Blessing and Preparation

It is my view that anyone awaiting a transplant should include in their preparation a blessing of the organ they may receive and the donor from whom it may come.

A client whose liver had collapsed as a consequence of a viral attack came to see me with just that in mind. She had read my earlier book, *Auras and Colours*, and was awaiting a liver transplant, but she was concerned that her deterioration might be such that she would die before a compatible organ became available. She was also wrestling with the guilt she felt that someone else would have to die that she might live.

First, we worked around the acceptance of an organ as a gift and a memorial from one who had, for whatever reason, vacated his body and to whom the liver would be of no further use. It became a gift, a bonus, a positive consequence of what, to some, would be a sadness. This is another illustration of life's amazing redemptive quality — however bad things may seem, there is always something better and good that can emerge.

Secondly, I taught her how to bless her body, and the existing liver, for its service to her, and how to bless the organ that would come her way, together with its donor. After one false alarm, a suitable liver was found for her and recent reports suggest that all is going very well indeed.

Exercise 1 — Attunement to Body Energy Blueprint
We should all be in touch with our body and its intelligent, energy or etheric support system. Sadly, we often neglect it until we are ill, often seriously. It is only then that we begin to pay any attention to such an idea. Like all relationships, this one needs to be nurtured and developed if it is to flourish, and the following exercise is designed to assist that nurturing:

1. Sit or lie quietly for a few moments, where you will not be disturbed.
2. Contemplate your physical body. However it is working now, be grateful for what it does for you. Bless it and thank it — it is a remarkable vehicle for your life.
3. Notice your breath, as your diaphragm stretches your lungs downwards to inhale the energising, restorative air. Feel the rhythm of this movement in your body as your stomach and abdomen rise upwards on the in breath and then relax in the breath's outward flow. Enjoy this for a few moments, allowing your breath to slow down as much as is possible and comfortable for you.
4. Be aware that your physical home, its organs, tissues and network of cells and atoms, are supported by this wonderful energy body which interpenetrates it and surrounds it. As you breathe, so this body absorbs energy and vitality from all around you, especially from the etheric/energy field of the earth and the sun. Imagine and feel it nurturing you, the flow between the two bodies being constant and powerful. Every cell in your body is now flowing with increased energy.

5. Remember that there is a perfect blueprint, or matrix, in your energy body for every organ and part of your physical self. Where you know there is a problem at the physical level, imagine the etheric/energy part of you connecting with that organ, joint, or tissue, in dynamic exchange with it, allowing it to form and to function properly. There is a continuous process active here. Old physical cells are continually being replaced by new ones, in harmony with the perfect information in the blueprint. Encourage that process and, in your mind, see it happening. Use your imagination — it is a powerful tool.

6. After a few moments, return to normal awareness by focusing on your feet as they touch the floor, or your body upon the bed. Feel connected with the earth and the physical life before you bring your focus and your attention around your eyes. Open them very slowly, as slowly as you can, before you move or stand up.

Such an attunement in itself is very healing and should be practised often. It is a simple way in which we can enhance the flow of life in us, and make a return journey to health and ease.

There are two other significant bodies in our human subtle anatomy.

The Emotional/Astral Body

The old alchemists called this the 'astral' body because the waves of colour, as they move within it, have an astral or star-like glow to them. This wonderful form, along with the etheric and mental bodies, I have viewed since my childhood. This form or body, which usually appears to psychics and mystics as oval in shape, is full of brilliant, fast-moving rays of coloured light. Within this light are many patterns, symbols and images, which are clothed by the emotional substance of this body.

Every human being, every animal, every flower and tree, every building — everything — has an emotional or astral body. This means that everything has the ability to express feeling and emotional nature. We all know how we can 'feel' the atmosphere of a building, a room, or even an antique or object that has accumulated a lot of emotional force around it.

We draw our emotional, astral substance from the astral plane of the earth around us, and the earth, in turn, draws in emotional forces from the solar emotional plane, and again, in turn, from the universal counterpart.

Each time we think, our thoughts move through this aspect of ourselves, attracting astral/emotional substance in accordance with how we feel about the thought or idea. This also has an enormous impact upon our ease and fall into disease, as we will consider later.

Our animal friends are heavily influenced by our own emotional natures, as they develop their own powerful emotional fields. We influence them more than we know. Recently it was acknowledged that some domestic pets seem to get depressed or anxious, and veterinary surgeons in the UK and the US are taking this very seriously, looking at ways of treating them. Barbara Woodhouse, that one-time doyenne of dog experts, always said that she never trained dogs, she trained their owners, as dogs absorb their attitudes and feelings largely from their owners!

The Mental Body

This body exists also around us in a super ovoid form. Again, full of brilliant, almost metallic, light, it is the body through which we think. The lower mental body is the point in our personalities where our thoughts become concrete and discernible. They form images, pictures or impressions that we can recognise.

The higher mental body is where our thoughts are abstract and non-concrete. It is not a part of our personality, but rather

24

a dynamic of our soul, or spiritual, higher self. It supplies fine concepts and inspirations which our concrete mind in our personality has to identify and differentiate. This process is known as the intuition, in its highest form, where the soul and higher mind seek to guide the personality, via its mind, brain and feelings, to live effectively. It also exists within the mental planetary, solar and universal mental planes.

The Vitality Stream

We are very blessed. There is a continuous stream of energy and vitality available for us, and it flows through our energy body in the following fashion:

Figure 2.2

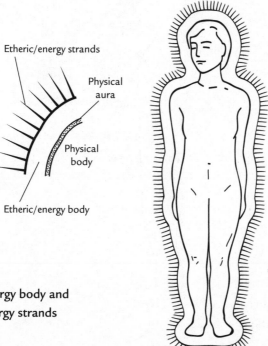

Etheric/energy strands

Physical aura

Physical body

Etheric/energy body

(a) Energy body and energy strands

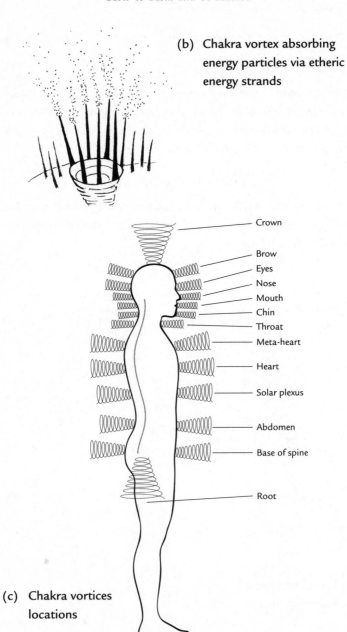

(b) Chakra vortex absorbing
energy particles via etheric
energy strands

Crown
Brow
Eyes
Nose
Mouth
Chin
Throat
Meta-heart
Heart
Solar plexus
Abdomen
Base of spine
Root

(c) Chakra vortices
locations

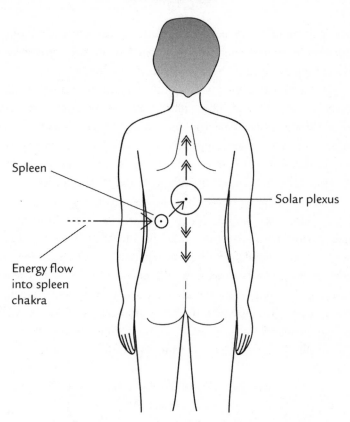

(d) Spleen chakra, moderating solar plexus chakra and then spinal energy flow

As we inhale, we draw vitality/energy in waves of particles through the hair-like radiation or absorption strands on the surface of our energy bodies. These strands direct the vitality particles into the energy body via the vortices (see Figure 2.2) known as chakras, or psychic centres. These vortices exist in the energy body close to groups of nerves called *nerve plexi* and glandular structures.

As the vitality is absorbed into the centre, it then flows along channels to the nearest nerve group or plexus to stimulate the nearby glandular system which, in turn, releases into the bloodstream the appropriate hormones needed for a healthy body. Hence the cycle of physical health is maintained.

The vitality streams are around us all the time and we breathe with our entire body. The vitality waves and particles are very visible and plentiful, especially on a sunny day. They dart around in our vision like fast-disappearing tadpoles. On a sunny day, we should take time to connect with this process, to see it and feel it coursing magically and unfailingly through our bodies.

Animals are good to watch in this respect, as are young, sleeping children and babies. They seem to be more efficient at absorption than many of us adults are. I have often observed my dog as she lies still, breathing deeply, the many chakra/centre vortices in her body welcoming the power of the vitality stream entering her body in an unending sequence of waves. A purring cat, in particular, is in effective absorption mode, which is why we can benefit from the presence of the young and animals when our vitality is lowered and wanting, especially in ill-health.

Figure 2.3: Chakra/Centre vortex overlay

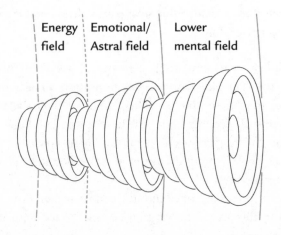

The major controlling movement of vitality is through a vortex or chakra close to the spleen, on the left of the body. It appears to govern the gearing and ability of all the other chakras as they seek to draw vitality into the body.

If the spleen and the solar plexus chakras are either under- or over-active for any reason, the whole system will also follow suit and general debility will ensue.

The chakra vortex network consists of the thirteen major centres (see Figure 2.2c), located along the spinal column and 440 minor centres across the surface of the human energy field. Each major centre is linked to forty smaller centres across the energy body, so there are, for example, one heart centre and forty minor heart centres all linked together, one throat centre and forty minor throat centres around the body, and so on.

The two exceptions are the crown centre and the root centre — they both link with all the minor centres in the body, linking Heaven (crown) and Earth (root) together in mankind. There is also a wonderful truth and ability that such a system gives to us — that whatever we do, we can do it with the whole of our being. Not only can we breathe and assimilate energy with the whole of our being, but we can also sing with every tissue in us, love with our whole being — we can be 'whole-hearted' about everything.

In the traditional Marriage Ceremony according to the Church of England's Book of Common Prayer, there is an interesting commitment that has its meaning enhanced by this knowledge in the words: 'with my body, I thee worship, with my entirety I honour you.'

When I was a schoolmaster, I belonged to several choirs. I was a good singer and I had briefly been a professional. Sometimes, on my return home from school, I would feel exhausted and really reluctant to go out again, despite loving my music deeply. However, after just a few minutes at rehearsal, I would be alive, energised, mentally clear and alert, and physically rejuvenated. I had sung not only with my throat, and breathing in much-needed extra vitality through my spleen and solar plexus, I had actually sung with my whole body. It had been a truly holistic experience — a great healing. If you like to sing, do so, often, and remember that you sing throughout your whole body.

Exercise 2 — The Chakra/Vortex Network
Good vitality flow can be maintained by this exercise, which should be repeated often, at least weekly.

1. Sit or lie comfortably where you will not be disturbed.
2. Focus upon your solar plexus centre for a few moments, just below your sternum in the centre of your ribcage. Gently encourage your breath to slow down a little, in a rhythmic, even movement. Slowly, think the words 'I breathe in' on each inhalation and 'I breathe out' as you release your breath. Your breath will gradually develop a slow rhythmic movement, flowing gently into your body, and then, after a pause, flowing slowly out again, with a brief pause before the next inhalation.
3. When you have practised this a few times, bring the focus of your attention to your Crown Chakra or centre. Imagine this vortex as it enters your energy body at the top of your head and focus your attention there as you take one slow, comfortable breath, drawing waves of vitality through the absorption strands, into the chakra and along a great web of channels, deep into your wonderful energy body. Do this three times, each time remembering that this process happens not only in the crown centre, but simultaneously in all the centres along the spine and across the vitality body.
4. Take your attention down to your root centre and visualise this vortex tapering upwards beneath the root of the spinal column. Here again, breathe deeply through the absorption

strands into the chakra, and then imagine the flow of vitality particles pouring along a great web of channels, through every major and minor centre in the energy body — all 453 of them. Do this three times, imagining and feeling the process as it energises every part of you. Encourage your imagination to show to you, as it surely will in time, the magic of this process in you.

5. Now move your focus up a little to the position of the chakra or centre (see Figure 2.2c) at the base of your spine. Imagine the vortex there, entering the front of your energy body and leaving at the rear of it. Direct one deep rhythmic breath through the absorption strands at the front of this centre, and out through the back. As you do this, encourage a picture to form in your mind of your base centre linked to a web of minor base centres across your entire energy field, vitalising you and healing you.

6. Repeat this visualisation using one deep breath through each of the other major chakras — the abdomen, the solar plexus, the heart, the meta heart, the throat, the chin, the mouth, the nose, the eyes and the brow. Remember not only to see this exercise with your imagination but also to *feel* it, using the sensitivity in your nervous system to do so. Some people will find the sensory approach easier at first.

7. Finally, return your attention to your crown centre. Imagine your body to be alive and alight, absorbing, processing and releasing energy through myriad beautiful whirling light centres in you. This exchange is dynamic and continuous, giving to you enormous reserves of power. You are really flowing as life flows now.

A Web of Light

Lucy was tired, anxious and depleted. She came to me because she and her husband were working all the hours they could to

31

develop their farm and their smallholding. He was also trying to hold down a job and she was supervising their young children.

A lovely young woman with a beautiful face, she wanted some help, desperately. She felt as if she was falling apart, and the perfectionist streak in her did not help when she saw so many shortcomings around her. She had no more energy and was extremely frustrated. There seemed to be little point in going on.

It was obvious to me just how disconnected she was. Her solar plexus spun slowly and erratically and I could see the stop–start shunting movement that is so common where people are simply exhausted. Of course, adjustments had to be made in the life pattern, and Lucy and her husband were seeking to make them. But how could I help?

As with all my clients, the self-healing aspect is crucial. With attunement and healing touch, I could stimulate her energy flow, but she needed most to heal herself, to call directly upon her own resources.

With a little practice, she quickly developed good, rhythmic breathing, and the vortices along her spine began to glow with the improved energy exchange as she accessed, assimilated and distributed energy with increasing efficiency. When she connected via her major centres to her energy network, the web of light was remarkable. A switch had been turned on in her — her spine shook and her cheeks flushed, just as if she had been wired into an electrical grid.

Lucy's energy body was a mass of glowing light and vibrant whirling vortices. As she opened her eyes, the power radiated around her. I had nothing else to do. Her energy was back and her subsequent renewed drive and purpose made great strides in her life possible. Their business grew and, after one or two more sessions, she maintained her increased energy levels very successfully indeed.

The Vortices

Our chakras or psychic centres perform a range of functions, the prime one being the management and absorption of powerful cosmic and universal forces. Performed effectively, this process provides the perfect blending and programming necessary for the expression or our individuality, each chakra being linked to a particular set of principles or forces.

At the *energy*, and its accompanying *physical*, level, the centres help us to exchange cosmic, solar and planetary energy to sustain physical form for our life on earth.

In the *astral* or *emotional* self, the centres enable us to process and engage with our feeling mechanism and psychic nature so that we can add particular qualities to our thoughts and be more conscious of them, as they flow through our minds. The centres at this level are currently very busy and we will look at our astral, emotional psychic self in more detail later.

In their highest expression, the astral centres open us to grand, generous feelings and expose us to beauty, joy, compassion and selflessness and a glimpse of love and universality. In their lowest expression, they cut us off from our most expansive awareness, allowing fear, limitation and destructiveness to rule. In current human terms, this is the seat of most of our difficulties.

In the *mental plane*, the chakras differentiate and process cosmic, mental forces. Here we are able to have unlimited knowledge, to be conscious of thought, to control our thinking, ideally learning how we may allow the thoughts expressing through our personality to be constructed as accurately as possible by our own soul or spiritual nature.

The lower part of our mental self is concrete, the level at which we recognise thoughts as either geometric forms or, more usually, as pictures or images. Sometimes these images become subliminal, expressing through our 'sentience' or feelings — in other words, we *feel* what is in our thoughts rather than *see* it.

One client of mine spoke for many when she told me that she could never 'see' anything in her head, or at least she was never aware of doing so. Her imagination always worked as a silent voice in her head or simply a sense of things occurring — but no vision!

At the higher mental level, the centres function in an abstract mode, so we appear to be 'not thinking', in some deeper state of inner reverie. We develop good access to this level via meditation and contemplation, where we are at the doorway to our soul as it seeks to show us how to think and how to build our lives here on earth. The chakras exist within us, in each of our bodies — etheric/energy, emotional/astral and mental — each interacting with the other in a wonderful overlay of potential (see Figure 2.3). In the physical body, the chakras manifest through glands and nerve plexi or groups.

This chakra alignment reflects the manner in which our being can function, guided perfectly for our stay on earth.

The Universal Connection

Universe >	Soul >	Mind >	Emotions >	Energy >	Physical
(spirit)	(individual spirit & higher mind)	(human mind to brain in thought)	(elevated feelings & high desires)	(power to enable physical expression)	(physical manifest-ation)

Our universal connection is vital in the manifestation of health, our experience of ease.

In this process, the spirit, individualised in our soul, seeks to express itself in us as it issues the perfect thought streams for us in our minds, in the pursuit of our role and destiny on the earth.

Our astral or emotional selves imbue our thoughts with the desire to be creative and active in the physical realm, and the energy they attract precipitates and builds our physical experience and the reality we explore, including our physical bodies.

In this marvellous connection, we re-enact the creation, allowing the universe to come into the physical world through us. A breakdown at any point in this process results in disease, the most common being in the emotional/astral self and body. The emotional body, as we will see later, often distorts and even blocks the thoughts our soul gives us, inhibiting, sometimes seriously, the possibility of a healthy, purposeful life.

Solar Angel

Through our soul or higher self, something very precious occurs and must be noted here as it is vital to our healing and the model I use. It concerns the Solar Angel, or the Angel of the Soul.

The perfect expression for us is known in the soul. It knows exactly what you and I are meant to be and how we can fulfil that purpose. Into our minds at birth it sends its message, with the perfect plan and unsullied information. This messenger is our own inner angel, or solar (soul) angel, as it is often called. It is the being of light in us all and its presence enables each human being to reveal divine light through its nature. The wonderful truth of this endowment is that, although we may not express perfection yet in our lives, we can certainly aspire to it and, with persistence, at least glimpse it.

In my teaching days, it never failed to amuse me when the parents of occasionally reluctant and tearful, small children would affirm, 'Mr Lambillion will look after you, my little angel.' Less than cherubic the 'little angel' may have appeared at that moment, but obviously, as loving parents, we recognise in our younger charges the golden light of the divine messenger — even on a bad day or in a moment of tension!

> *The Soul that rises with us, our life's Star,*
> *Hath elsewhere its setting,*
> *And cometh from afar:*

Not in entire forgetfulness,
And not in utter nakedness,
But trailing clouds of Glory do we come
From God, who is our home.

Wordsworth

That Glory is our Solar, inner Angel, guardian of our perfection, however obscure. In any healing process, the role of the Solar Angel is crucial, as we will consider later on.

Exercise 3 — The Universal Connection
We should take a few moments to affirm this transcendental truth in us.

1. Practise the simple rhythmic breathing as in Exercise 2.
2. When your breath is deep and even, focus your attention at the crown of your head, imagining a bright beam of light pouring downwards through your head, along your spinal column to the root centre.
3. Imagine this light radiating through every level of your being — your physical, energistic, emotional, mental and spiritual selves. You are in the centre of it.
4. Upon this light is borne a beautiful messenger, who rides upon it as it issues from the Spirit of the Universe, through your soul and into your mind, linking you and eternity in a wise and loving embrace.
5. Imagine this perfect universal presence to be within you, guiding your thoughts and feelings, and connecting your physical nature and your personality with the highest possibilities for you in this life. Begin to sense the ease this brings to you, the healing it initiates. From universe to soul, soul to mind, mind to feelings and feelings through to energy and body.

6. Finally, be aware of your Solar Angel and the divine intelligence encapsulated in its nature, as it engineers the relationship between your soul nature and your personality.
7. Return to normal consciousness, slowly, bringing with you the memory of your Universal Connection.

Pam's Story

Pam and her husband were a truly devoted couple and they were looking forward to some well-earned retirement time together. When I met Pam, she was beginning to develop a keen interest in matters spiritual, and had become a voracious reader of metaphysical and natural healing books and literature.

A bad experience with another therapist had sent her in my direction, basically for some reassurance and support. Shortly after our meeting, her husband was diagnosed with advanced liver cancer. The prognosis was poor and, a few days before retirement from his work, he died.

Pam was bereft. Surrounded by the debris from broken dreams, and contemplating the prospect of years of loneliness ahead, she herself became unwell. She started to have stomach problems, and an ulcer was suspected. Her spine also began to give her problems and locked near the base, severely restricting her mobility.

One day, during a healing session, we did a little meditation together, designed to link her with her own power and its universal source. I made no mention to her of angels and guides, simply guiding her in general terms as I usually do.

That night, she had what she described as a 'healing dream'. During deep sleep, she met her husband who assured her that he was well in his new life. He then disappeared from view, and before her was a being who radiated the most incandescent golden light. It was a kind of angel, she felt, yet it also seemed inexplicably to be a part of her — something so beautiful, so wonderful and peaceful.

Upon awakening the next morning, Pam had changed. She felt that this 'inner angel' had spoken to her. What it had said she couldn't recall, but she was compelled to get on with something, to begin anew. Gradually, her stomach griping ceased, and her back loosened up. She went off to train as a counsellor — and then other things besides. When I last heard of her some years ago, she was busy in her practice.

She was at ease again.

A Study of Centre Meanings and Correspondence

In a journey from dis-ease back into ease, a little deeper knowledge of the chakra or psychic centre vortices is useful, as an understanding of them will reveal much to us about the causes of our disease. Their effective function is essential in the pursuit of health.

As with many correspondences, once we consider the levels in us beyond three dimensions, and search into fourth and fifth dimensional realities, there are no absolutes, but rather interweaving possibilities. Because we are a unified being, an entire universe within ourselves, everything in us is linked to everything else. Every thought we have, every action we take, has an effect, not only in ourselves and upon our immediate reality, but onwards throughout the universe.

> *All things by immortal power*
> *Near or far*
> *Hiddenly*
> *To each other linked are,*
> *That thou canst not stir a flower*
> *Without troubling of a star.*
>
> Francis Thompson

Nothing is separate or isolated, and the functions of the chakra vortices overlap considerably. However, the following ideas and correspondences will help us to understand the disease and consequent healing patterns in us, as we relate more dynamically to our multi-dimensional nature.

Root Centre and Base Centre

These vortices, which absorb the energy and light of purpose, are at the seat of our physical nature. The root centre literally keeps us earthed and, at death, it is the first centre to close and cease to function. In the base centre, we retain our primordial memory and our relationship with our inherent animal nature and the animal kingdom. The physical organs especially linked with these two centres are the kidneys and the adrenal glands, along with the spinal column.

This lower area is the seat of will, the will-to-be, and our birth and incarnation are generated by the forces of these marvellous vortices.

The Physical Kundalini, the most commonly perceived of the three divine fires, emanates from them and kindles in us the drive and determination necessary to reach out to the Universe through our human endeavour. Both centres have a special relationship with the heart centre, and the dynamic of love and goodness, as we seek to use our drive, pursuing good ideas and projects — the will-to-good as it is often called. Undercharging produces lack of determination, and a sense of pointlessness to life, whilst overcharging makes the individual pushy and aggressive in dealings with others.

A Reflection

Before you move on, pause for a moment and take a few deep breaths. Reflect on the remarkable nature of these two centres and how they absorb the forces that enable you to exist at all in the physical world. Breathe deeply, and consider the key ideas here: the will-to-be and determination.

The Abdominal Centre

An amazing vortex, here is our connection with the etheric/ energy plane and our opportunity to focus our power and energy effectively. This centre also has a connection with sexuality. Our sexuality and generative organs have a direct correspondence with the effective functioning of this centre. If it works well, our vitality is good and, generally, our energy levels will keep us healthy. We will have healthy, balanced attitudes to our own sexuality and that of others. Linking with the solar plexus centre above it and the spleen centre, a super-chakra is formed, often referred to as the hara, giving to us enormous energetic and healing potential.

The abdominal vortex also connects with our throat centre to give us power for mental creativity. When this centre is under-active, we lack energy, have no sexual drive, and we are generally uninspired and dull. When overcharging, we become mentally and emotionally starved, and there is always a risk of promiscuity and sexual disease. We often use this centre and its forces to manipulate and control.

Key Words for Reflection: Power and Creativity
Take a space to consider your absorption and utilisation of energy from the Universe. Breathe deeply and reflect upon the key words.

Solar Plexus

When the telephone rings, or a letter drops on the mat, or you enter a strange room encountering new people, the solar plexus springs into dynamic action, managing our initial reaction to the experience.

This centre is a meeting point in us between the material (physical and energistic) world, the emotional (astral) planes, and our higher nature. It is often described as a clearing house for our emotions, and its link with the heart centre enables us to refine our feelings and emotions — in effect, to absorb, digest and, where necessary, detoxify our emotional experiences. In the physical body, the solar plexus links with our nervous system, stomach and digestive system, liver, gall bladder and pancreas — the physical organs of experience, absorption, digestion and detoxification and sweetness.

The solar plexus chakra also has a strong connection with our understanding of space and geometry. Surprisingly, for many, the geometric analysis this centre makes for us in its measurement of space enables us to drive a car along a road (our eyes deceive us and the perspective suggests that the road ahead narrows, but the solar plexus tells us that this is an illusion and it's safe to go on). The centre helps us to understand space. Sportsmen also use the solar plexus to judge distance, and many a good tennis serve or football pass owes as much to this vortex as it does to the eye!

The Mental Kundalini, which acts as a balance between the physical fire in the root and base centres and the divine light that expresses in us at our crown centre, has its own focus in our mental bodies close to this centre, along with the throat centre.

Dowsers especially use the solar plexus, as do psychics, to read energetic and emotional information. Our solar plexus can determine the basic quality of the telephone call or letter before we read it, and send signals to our brain via the adjacent nerve plexus and the vagus nerve to our hearts. How often have the butterflies in your stomach given to you an important 'gut' feeling, some useful subtle guidance or insight in relation to a new experience or a choice to be made? This is the seat of our 'fight or flight' responses.

When working efficiently in such situations, your wonderful solar plexus is in its glory. Unfortunately, in many it is either extremely under-active, precipitating low-energy disease, such as ME and cancer, or overcharging, causing anxiety states, emotional chaos, eating disorders, obesity and diabetes. It also helps us, along with the abdomen and the spleen centres, to process energy. For humanity, in these fast-changing times, it is a key centre, as many of our health problems emanate from here.

Key Words for Reflection: Desire, Need and Feeling

Take a few deep breaths. In the warmness of the moment, consider the energies and forces absorbed and processed by this centre, the connection with feelings, emotions, your creative desires and objectives. Consider how it helps you to integrate the energies of new places and experiences in your life.

Heart Centre

When all else fails, we usually return to love. In moments of tragedy, death, pain and fear, we often catch a glimpse of how important love is to us. Any denial of love is our denial of ourselves, for human beings are designed to be centres of love and wisdom.

The heart vortex has physical correspondences with the physical heart and its attendant circulatory system, the blood stream, and the vagus nerve, which effectively links the heart with the solar plexus.

Through our hearts we learn to love, to have compassion and empathy, and it is effectively in the centre of us in every sense — physical, energetic, mental, emotional and universal. We can live without most things, but not without a heart, and it is no coincidence that at the centre of most religious teaching is the propagation of love. It is the seat of group consciousness and inclusivity.

An overcharging heart gives us allergies, asthma, heart attacks and strokes; a slow heart may precipitate arthritis, heart degeneration and circulatory disease.

We express our higher feelings through our heart chakra, along with our higher divine or spiritual minds. It is also part of our intuitive mechanism and the focus of understanding and generosity. Love, through the heart, understands and is kind. This centre has strong links with the head centre (intuition) and the root centre (the will-to-(be) good and loving), and we can think properly only when the heart centre is involved.

Key Words for Reflection: Love and Wisdom

The forces of the universe and the higher mental worlds are absorbed by you through this centre. The heart chakra makes you adaptable, able to change, to grow and to let go. You hug life with this centre, knowing that everyone and everything is valuable, and important. Reflect on that for a moment.

Meta Heart Vortex

An emerging chakra, this centre connects us with honesty and openness, and interacts powerfully with the heart, the higher mental plane, exalted thinking, and our soul. As this centre unfolds, so the human predilection for secrecy, and even deceit, dissolves. Hiding and concealing things is a feature of the past; our future demands openness, transparency. Liars and money launderers beware — consensus is the way forward. As with the heart vortex, there are strong connections with the physical heart and also the skin/epidermis. Undercharging of this centre manifests as dishonesty and degenerative conditions of all kinds. Overcharging produces gullibility, naiveté and susceptibility to virus and infections.

Key Words for Reflection: Honesty and Truth

These are important key words for the meta heart. Take your deep rhythmic breaths and sense the flow of truth pouring into your system. This centre links with the heart and pineal gland (crown centre), producing a super-chakra which is the intuitive vortex — the space in which our destiny unfolds.

Throat, Mouth and Nasal Centres

The throat vortex opens us to our concrete mind, through which we connect with and absorb the energies and forces of creativity, communication and memory. Under-functioning throats produce laziness, a mental lethargy which in turn becomes physical, poor perception, and weak self-expression and dialogue. Over-charging in this centre leads to talkative, over-sensitive, nervous individuals, with defensiveness in behaviour patterns and a tendency to hyperventilate and experience breathing difficulties. Over-charging here is also common in religious fanatics and preachers, often leading to sexual dis-function because of strong links between the throat and the abdomen chakras. The mouth and nasal centres also have dynamic connections with the quality of our self-expression.

The physical connections are with the mouth, ears and alimentary canal, the lungs and the diaphragm. Thyroid problems are throat-based, as are lung disease and hiatus hernias.

Key Words for Reflection: Mental Creativity and Perfect Self-expression

Breathe slowly and deeply. Reflect upon these ideas and the way the universe pours its creative mind through these vortices so that you may express yourself powerfully and creatively with clear articulation. Remember how powerful your words are and how you can both heal and destroy with them. We should always communicate with sensitivity and calm awareness.

Brow and Eyes

These are two key vortices absorbing forces of vision, recognition and integration. They help us to see, both on the inside (brow and crown link with pineal gland) with our imagination, and on the outside, in our three-dimensional world, with our eyes and optic nerve. Constant over-charging here causes migraine, some headaches, strokes and epilepsy, whilst under-charging will precipitate mental lethargy, tumours and eye problems.

The brow chakra, in particular, is extremely magnetic and draws information upwards from the lower centres both to integrate it and to interpret it, then offering it, via the crown centre, up to our soul or higher self for processing, before it determines our best and most suitable future thoughts and actions. Our whole concept of time is governed from here.

Physically, the most significant links are with the brain, left eye, nervous system and pituitary gland — hence our physical growth. Clairvoyant vision (and so-called hallucination) is a direct consequence of the functioning of these two centres, and when, through meditation, aspiration and prayer, we link with the universal light in our crown centre, effectively, our eye is truly 'single and our body will be full of light.'

These centres link with the soul or higher self (the eyes are viewed as the windows of the soul and they can often reveal when someone is approaching death, even days before the transition takes place.) When the heart and the crown are effectively connected, the intuitive flow is complete with them, and we are able to think in our hearts as we should.

Key Words for Reflection: Vision, Integration, Recognition and Soul

Take time now to reflect upon these chakras. When focusing your breath here, consider the miracle of sight — both inner and outer vision — and how we have the capacity to recognise, remember and discriminate. Think how you can open to your soul and the process of learning and awakening through which your soul will lead you safely when you allow it to do so.

These are remarkable centres, awakening us to a new relationship with our multi-dimensional nature and our capacity to create our experiences consciously. They are developing very rapidly in us now, sometimes prompting a sense of unreality in these fast-changing times. My 17-year-old son has said to me many times recently that life seems to be increasingly surreal and dreamlike. This is the consequence of the rapid time adjustments these centres are asked to make.

The Crown Centre

The crown centre is magnificent.

This is where the spirit touches you and me, and the universe seeks to make intelligent contact with our human nature.

The significant physical correspondences are the brain, the right eye and the pineal gland, and when this gland is properly linked with the pituitary gland, the divine and the human begin to engage and be at one — the seat of at-one-ment, when human will and divine will merge: 'thy will be done, on earth, as it is in Heaven.' The crown is very active until adolescence when its influence fades somewhat and usually does not become significant until later in life when our sense of immortality has diminished and our thoughts (and ideally actions) tend to return to spiritual ideas and deeper meanings.

Many schools of thought believe that the fontanel, the soft spot on the skull which 'heals over' when we grow, is a residual reminder of an earlier time when we had a respiratory system more in line with that of the dolphins and whales. In those times, we channelled air through the skull, past the pineal gland, rather than bypassing it as it does now. Much of our religious tradition encourages an openness in the skull — trepanning, monastic tonsure and so on — and the skull is very significant in many esoteric traditions.

Children born with jaundice need extra high-frequency light upon their pineal glands. It was common for parents who were students of the esoteric and occult to request that their newly born offspring have their hair shaved from the skull so that the light could still stimulate the glands in the head, awakening them to their true spiritual nature whilst upon the earth.

If this centre is not effective, we feel disconnected from life, cut-off and isolated, no matter how many people we may have around us in the physical world. This disconnection is pivotal in both the manner and nature of our death: when we are fully connected, our death is a conscious activity for which we prepare and in which we willingly participate; when we are disconnected, our death is often painful, fearful and apparently random — an event over which we have no control.

Key Words for Reflection: Light, Spirit, Divine Will and Connection

The higher fire awakens in us from the crown blending with the mind (solar plexus and throat) and mental fire, the body (root/base centre) and physical kundalini, enabling the manifestation of Perfected Mankind.

A View of Causes

On our journey into ease, there are many phenomena to consider. Some, such as chemical pollution through poor or even reckless industrial and pharmaceutical practice, along with agricultural and food toxicity, are beyond the remit of this book and my immediate work, but vigilance in these areas must be encouraged.

However, it has long been my view — and, as a consequence of my experience, it is even more so — that our priorities should be in an effective synthesis, fusing energetic good practice, emotional and mental clarity and spiritual awareness.

If we achieve this integration, or at least work towards it, our healing will take with a new, intelligent and limitless dynamism, opening doors that have hitherto been closed and giving back to us the power we have long since surrendered.

Solar and Planetary

Our planet is changing. And so is our sun. The incidence of solar storms, usually between thirty and forty a year, has risen since the 1980s to up to several hundred even in a month. Measurements of the electro-magnetic field of the sun by various NASA probes during the 1990s have suggested that the sun's polarity is in an usual state of flux, making the usual polarity measurements difficult to maintain.

I remember reading in the *Daily Telegraph* a few years ago, just before I was about to fly to the city of Edinburgh, that a problem had been experienced by some incoming aircraft. The difficulty was caused by a particularly unusual, significant shift in the magnetic field of the earth, interfering with the relationship between aircraft instruments and the approach markings on the ground. Adjustments had to be made to cope with the changes, and I was mightily relieved that this had been noticed and dealt with before my arrival! The airport is very close to the River Forth.

The magnetic field of the planet, directly influenced by the solar field, is also weakening, as well as shifting.

Research in Japan by Dr Kyoichi Nakagawa, from as early as 1976, suggests that there is a growing magnetic-field deficiency on the planet, affecting the health and well-being of people (and animals). My own vision concurs with this, and the effects upon our physical bodies are likely to be far-reaching and profound.

There is now a feeling that this field is at its lowest in human history and, in my view, it is largely responsible in whole or in part for many of the energetic diseases, such as ME, fatigue, some cancers, depressions, extreme vitality fluctuations, and a desire for more sleep, which often proves ultimately to be inadequate, however much we have. So many clients come to me complaining of wild, inexplicable fluctuations in energy, and that no sleep, however long, proves particularly refreshing.

The growth in magnetic therapy is a response to this gradual depletion. Some of this therapy is useful, and I have observed the effects of magnetic therapy upon the human aura and energy field, and subsequently, the human body.

However, it should be applied only occasionally, with care, and isn't universally helpful. We will address these issues later in the book.

Environmental

One client who came to see me was experiencing the most unusual stomach problems. No pathological cause had been discovered — an increasingly common phenomenon today, as energetic illness grows in our society. He was experiencing cramps, usually precipitating sudden falls in energy, and, occasionally, feelings of panic, sometimes briefly freezing him with fear.

He was a down-to-earth individual who worked for the electricity board. He enjoyed sport, and especially liked to relax by walking in the countryside and, in the season, fishing in nearby rivers and streams.

His solar plexus was exhibiting the most unusual behaviour, fluctuating from an over-charging fast rotation, to a rapid slowing and, very occasionally, almost freezing altogether, motionless. Something to which he had been exposed had placed him in shock, but a detailed exploration of his personal life revealed nothing of note that would have initiated the problem.

Then he revealed that he had been on a training programme which had included long periods in a nuclear power station. I remembered some words of the radionics practitioner, the late Dr David Tansley, who noticed that individuals who worked in or near such establishments often displayed, in the chakra system, symptoms resembling shock. My patient's work-training also coincided with the onset of these problems — problems which had ultimately been blamed upon a mysterious virus.

My subsequent working with him gradually eased the problem, modulating the movement of his solar plexus centre sufficiently to increase his energy flow safely and permanently.

Increasing environmental radiation and wave pollution is now widespread. It comes at us at all levels — electromagnetics, radio, TV, microwaves, telephone masts, and so on to infra red and beyond the visible spectrum through to X-rays, gamma rays and a whole gamut of forces. Sometimes, we adapt to these bombardments, but often we don't, and they drain us, precipitating energy depletion and placing us at risk of serious disease in our physical bodies. Yet, awareness of these things and good practice will help us to offset them and to live with them.

The networks of electric cable conducting many lines of current through sundry buildings, our homes, workplaces and transport, in turn create complex wave fields which can, and do, affect our assimilation of vitality. We need to be aware of these fields and to engage with them effectively, neutralising any harmful effect they may have upon us.

Emotional Turbulence

Perhaps the greatest source of disruption we are dealing with is in our emotional fields.

Pharmaceutical psycho-active prescribing and treatments are now widespread, and many physicians find themselves under assault from patients either requiring emotional calming from anxiety states as their emotional bodies over-charge and become too electrical, or needing a lift from their depressions as their under-charging emotional/astral selves become weak and spasmodic. If the stop–start effect becomes too pronounced, manic states manifest, presenting extreme fluctuations in mood and behaviour.

There are two patterns involved for us to note.

Our Individual Patterns

So much of our conduct is governed by fear and our poor connection with life (cf. crown chakra). We have, over generations, been rendered powerless by our sense of limitation, and it takes a bold soul to reach out beyond the normal boundaries, to dare to test life and not be afraid of the unknown.

In fact, the emotional debris we are now seeking to clear stems from our ignorance and misunderstanding of who we really are. As a consequence, there is a tussle taking place in us as we seek to heal our individual selves and eradicate the sense of isolation so many of us experience — issues based in the solar plexus — and integrate that process into the unfolding of a new, more meaningful collective human consciousness in which we can healthily and creatively participate. We yearn for the love, the sense of belonging and community that such awareness gives to us, yet the communities of the past have so often let us down, seeming at best to ignore us, and at worst to manipulate and harm us. We have to grow beyond the confines of accepted wisdom — both individually and collectively — if we are to survive, which I am certain we will, dwelling more in the actions of our hearts.

The powers that be may prefer us to stay where we are — afraid and dependent as they run our lives for us. The emerging changes, however, will not allow that, and those leaders who feel that they can still rule us in the old ways are, happily, mistaken.

I admire the wonderful work being done by a growing band of counsellors and psychotherapists, assisting in the process of healing the emotional body. But, in our understanding of the following key relationship and its mechanism, we will promote so much profound and permanent healing in us.

Exercise 4 — Heart and Solar Plexus

We will consider this idea in more detail later on, but, for a moment, it is useful to make an initial link with the process.

1. Sit or lie quietly, away from distractions, and focus upon your breathing.
2. Establish slow, rhythmic breathing as in Exercise 2, and then slowly link the chakras or centres at the crown of your head and the root of your spine with a beam of beautiful, clear light, radiating along your spinal column. Draw this beam downwards from top to bottom, allowing your imagination to flourish.
3. Imagine that beam of light gradually expanding and radiating throughout each of your bodies — the physical, the energetic, the emotional/astral and the mental, until you are indeed a centre of clear light, radiating all around you.
4. Bring your attention back to your spinal column and to the solar plexus vortex. As you focus on this chakra, reflect upon your individuality, your personality. Gently sound your name.
5. Allow your attention to glide upwards to the vortex of your heart, lifting your name into it as you do so. Reflect here upon the community of life — the human family of which you are a part; the planet, the solar system and beyond.
6. Think of moments of great love, both when you have been loved by another and also those moments in which you have experienced love flowing through you out into life. Enjoy the sense of belonging. Say thank you for what you feel.
7. Bring your consciousness back to normal awareness, slowly connecting with the earth through your feet, and then the space around you, before you open your eyes.

Collective Emotional Patterns

A famous politician said recently, 'You are either with us or against us.' That is emotional blackmail of the worst kind, and we live in a culture where such emotional manipulation is rife.

A few years ago, Diana, Princess of Wales, died tragically in a road accident. Much has been said and written about the time and I don't wish to add to that unnecessarily. None the less, it was an interesting, if at times troubling, episode. For many, there was a genuine outpouring of grief as they linked their own emotional issues with those of the icon that Diana had become and the loss of something so apparently beautiful yet vulnerable. In mourning Diana, they mourned the lost innocence and hidden beauty in themselves. The widespread devotion to the idea of Diana had resulted in extreme shock and pain, as such sometimes obsessive devotion will. It was a truly remarkable seven days and I am certain there was much emotional healing taking place in our society.

Sadly, there was also a darker side, as those who did not share the same emotional enthusiasm for the event were persecuted. A local hairdresser was harangued for opening her salon on the morning of the funeral to keep a long-standing appointment with a wedding party — bride and bridesmaids — due to have their marriage celebrated that afternoon. Such emotional extremism is fanatical and dangerous. If you didn't at least appear to go with the crowd on the emotional tide, you were wrong, and no debate was to be countenanced.

Many used the occasion to vent their own anger, to rage at their own misplaced guilt. And we witnessed a remarkable period. From the Sunday when the event occurred, to the seventh day, the Saturday of the funeral, the nation, and indeed much of the world, travelled through shock to anger, from anger to despair, and from despair to examination, and, eventually, to the emergence of conciliation and healing.

I believe a significant emotional clearing took place during that time and, in life's wonderful, redemptive way, things will never be the same again.

At the time of writing, the world is recovering from the

emotional shock in the aftermath of the disaster when two air-liners were deliberately flown into the World Trade Center twin buildings in New York. Amongst the many wonderful stories that emerge during such a painful time, is the messages from those individuals who managed to make last-minute phone calls just before they died in the horrific events — both from within the crashing planes, or when hopelessly trapped in a doomed skyscraper. Most, if not all, of the messages expressed the love of the one who was about to die for those who were left behind. In our anger, we should remember that.

Our individual emotional experiences are both gleaned from and conditioned by those of the groups within which we function. Whilst we inject our own emotional responses into the human emotional field, so, in turn, we are emotionally the products of the times and lives we have experienced. If we are determined, we can let go of that.

And it is in our hearts that we find the vital key to our healing, as we release our collective emotional patterns and experiences, and our own individualised fears and concerns that arise within them.

Mental Bombardment

'A poor life this if, full of care, we have no time to stand and stare,' said William Henry Davies. What a great insight that is.

Our lack of ease is further compounded by mental bombardment — we are going into information overload. There is a continuous stream of information being thrown at us from the media — oh for the days of one TV channel and a few radio stations to choose from!

Privacy is stripped away from us. Phones and e-mails continually demand our attention, and the curse of the uncontrolled mobile phones wreaks havoc in restaurants, cinemas, concerts, conversations and intimate moments of all kinds.

Taking space to do nothing is viewed with either suspicion or disdain. If you are not 'busy', you are not functioning.

The relationship between 'closed' and 'open' consciousness is not understood properly, if at all, and we are not given space to think and reflect. Yet, it is in those moments that we open ourselves laterally to the innovations and solutions that our linear thinking cannot find. This idea is beautifully illustrated in a training video for industry, presented by the comedian and actor, John Cleese. He relates how the ignorant boss chastises his employees who seem to be daydreaming and not beavering away furiously at some more obvious endeavour.

I use the words 'reflect' and 'consider' often in this book, and that is quite deliberate. We need, at times, to reflect and be free and expansive in our thinking, as well as, at other times, to be focused and intellectually linear.

I once went to a breakfast business meeting and I found it simply awful. People talked and negotiated as they scoffed food, answered phone calls and had one eye on the clock in case it all over-ran the schedule. Nothing was focused upon properly or given the attention and respect it deserved. Neither was there space for reflection. We can never be truly at ease whilst we live in such a way, and breakdown may be just around the corner.

Checking in at an airport recently, I was behind a man who was talking to a colleague whilst using his mobile phone to send a text message, as the desk clerk asked for his ticket and fired security questions at him. Not only is this rude, it is a recipe for disaster. It is a recipe for disease.

But you are not limited by such behaviour. You can be at ease.

The Spiritual Desert

In western society at least, there is a gradual desertion of dogmatic religion, and even those who still attend their weekly church, synagogue or whatever, tend more and more frequently to bend the rules to suit themselves, in a way my own devout Catholic mother would have found intolerable. At the local Catholic Upper School my children attended, less than 15 per cent of the children are now active in their religious practice. Such a possibility would have been unthinkable in my youth.

Recently, a young British Muslim woman told me how, whilst she still had respect for the essence of her religion, she felt that she could no longer entirely endorse much of the teaching her parents followed. She had long been aware of a need for something else — a greater vision that reached beyond the boundaries of conventional and transient religious doctrine and dogmas.

Recent surveys suggest that most people in the United Kingdom still believe in a God of some kind, whilst not endorsing or following a particular religious practice. The yearning is still there, if the appropriate support structure and discipline are not.

My experience has left beyond question the existence of a higher or spiritual dimension to man, and I believe that we cannot be healed or whole unless we at least acknowledge that dimension of ourselves and involve it in our process.

Many find that their healing is, indeed, a spiritual experience for them, the beginning of a journey, and they learn through it to develop a new relationship with their source and their spiritual nature.

In the next chapter we will explore the healing such connection can bring — the finding of the oasis of the soul in the spiritual desert.

CHAPTER 3

HEALING IN THE ENERGY BODY

Mary's Story

Mary wrote to me prior to her visit, as some folk do, so I'd have a clearer idea of her problem, and could cancel her visit if I felt she was 'being silly' and maybe 'going a little mad.'

Her words, however, recounted a story that, in one form or another, I hear increasingly.

> I have always thought that I was 'not here' properly, even as a child. It seemed I needed anchors in my shoes and my mum always said that I was 'away with the fairies' … One way or another, I have managed these odd detached feelings, through some yoga, regular acupuncture and praying to whatever God there happens to be. Recently, however, these experiences have returned, more powerfully than ever before. I now feel wobbly, disorientated, as if I'm somehow living on the edge of myself, not in the centre anymore. I walk into things — chairs and tables, and occasionally I feel as if I'm about to leave my body completely. My energy fluctuates … and I'm now simply not coping. Medical tests have revealed nothing significant and maybe you may think I am being silly ….

Mary certainly wasn't a fool. And her observations were truly revealing, giving a clear indication of where the problems were based and how we might begin to deal with them.

When we met, Mary was quite relieved that, at last, someone might not only believe her, but also, perhaps, give her some real help on her journey to recovery. A common feature of energetic disease which has yet to produce observable pathology in the physical body is that the sufferer feels isolated, bewildered and afraid of being the butt of criticism and ridicule from those around them, including, sometimes, medical professionals who should know better. I know this from my own experience, as well as from the many cases I have observed.

Mary's mental aura was quite beautiful, indicating a sensitive, intelligent woman, and, considering her current challenges, her astral or emotional aura did not indicate the level of depressive or anxiety states one might have expected to see. The suggested tranquillizers and anti-depressants prescribed would have been of no long-term use to her, and might eventually have made the situation worse. Whilst perhaps providing a limited short-term benefit, such psychoactive medication damages further the coping mechanism in the nervous system and the energetic and emotional bodies, whilst weakening the patient further through chemical pollution and possible addiction.

Magnetic Disruption

However, the energy body told a slightly different story. Although Mary was absorbing energy reasonably effectively, she was releasing it too quickly, without processing it properly through to her nerves and nervous system. This was leading to a weakness or fatigue in the solar plexus, and a general lack of stability in the relationship between the lower part of her energy body and her physical body. This accounted for her disconnected feeling. It had been with her, to some extent, since birth, and was now exacerbated by the weakening planetary magnetic field and her poor alignment to it.

We all need to have this alignment working effectively, or,

increasingly, we will feel out of things, misaligned and not properly 'earthed', with uncontrolled, fluctuating power levels coursing through us.

Figure 3.1: Magnetic field patterns

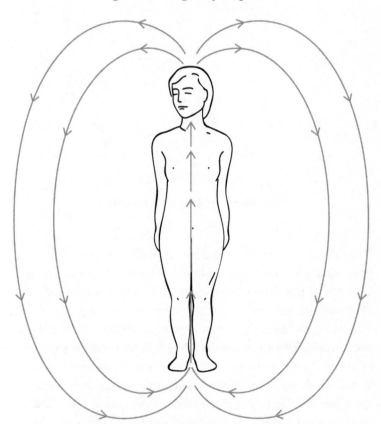

(a) Human Magnetic Force Pattern

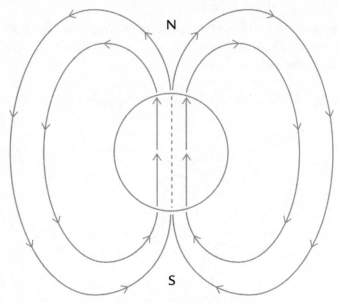

(b) **Planetary Magnetic Pattern**

I could see that Mary's magnetic rhythm was quite irregular, producing a distorted pattern in the magnetic flow through her and around her. As a consequence, there was a lack of balance, especially the feeling that she was living 'on the edge of myself'. This is an increasingly common experience for many people, and is particularly common in children. It often has ramifications in the emotional and mental bodies because the magnetism in us is the stabilising, earthing influence that makes our electrical thoughts and feelings manageable. Without it, we find it increasingly difficult to control our thinking and feeling as Mary had struggled to do.

The urgent remedy was based upon a simple process — most healing processes are essentially simple — and was one that I had originally developed to help me overcome jet lag on long-haul transatlantic flights.

Exercise 5 — Magnetic Alignment — Coping with Magnetic Stress

This is a simple exercise which, in these times of enormous magnetic flux and change in the planet itself, should be practised often by everyone. A key exercise, it is given in two forms, because, for practical reasons, we cannot always easily find a space where we can lie on an exact magnetic north–south axis.

FORM 1
Stage 1
For this exercise you will need a compass and a soft mat or mattress to lie on.

1. With your compass, find an alignment that runs from magnetic north to magnetic south. Then, lie down with the top of your head pointing north and the base of your spine pointing to the south. Ensure that you are comfortable, so that you can concentrate adequately on the process without distraction.
2. *Finding the Centre* — this is an important exercise and will be referred to often as you progress through this book.
   (a) Breathe rhythmically, saying slowly in your head the words 'I breathe in' as you inhale through your nostrils, and 'I breathe out' as you exhale. With practice, this becomes easy to do.
   (b) Gently lift your attention to the crown of your head and imagine a point of clear light there. Draw a line with this light, slowly downwards until you reach the root of the spine. Now you have a beam of light through the centre of your being. Again, with practice, this will become easier.
   (c) Imagine that beam of light becoming gradually brighter and brighter, so that its beautiful clarity radiates through

every level of you — physical, energetic, astral/emotional and mental. You have become a wonderful centre of light, radiating all around.

When you have mastered this part of the exercise, progress to Stage 2.

Stage 2

Figure 3.2: Human and planetary magnetic overlay

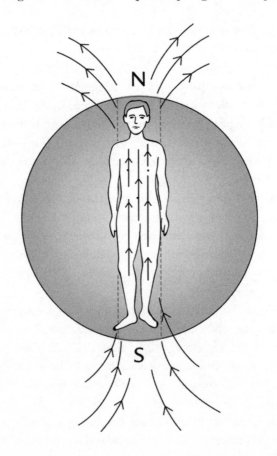

1. Return your attention to the central column of light in you, remembering that your head is aligned to the north magnetic pole and your feet to the south. In your mind's eye build a picture of this alignment (see Figure 3.2) with your own magnetic and energetic axis overlaying perfectly the magnetic axis of the planet. Allow the two fields to merge.
2. Focusing on the space between your heart centre and the crown of your head, breathe rhythmically for at least five minutes, sensing and imagining the strengthening of your own magnetic field as you attune deeply to the earth.
3. When this is completed, slowly and carefully turn yourself around until your crown is pointing southwards and your feet to the north. Again, breathe rhythmically, this time focused upon the space from your heart to the base of your spine and down to the soles of your feet. Repeat this for the same duration as you did in part 2, allowing yourself to connect with the planet once more and with its powerful, balancing magnetic flow.
4. When you have completed this, return to your original position, this time linking your whole spinal light from head to root centre with that of the earth. Again, breathe rhythmically for just a few minutes before awakening slowly.
5. Very gradually, sit up, and then stand with your feet a few inches apart. Stretch, raising the palms of your hands upwards, as if to touch the ceiling. Do this three times, breathing in deeply as you stretch and exhaling as you relax.

FORM 2: SUBJECTIVE ALIGNMENT

For obvious reasons, we cannot always do this lying down, or indeed actually in north–south alignment. So, there is an alternative method, which, if not always quite as effective, is still very useful and should be employed when the other method is not possible. For this method:

1. Practise the finding-the-centre exercise as in the first form, but this time seated on a chair.
2. In your mind, imagine the sphere of the earth, its wonderful magnetic field, with its axis travelling like a line north to south.
3. Visualise your own north to south, from crown to root-centre magnetic axis and its wonderful field of flow (Figure 3.1).
4. Imagine your axis to be in perfect alignment with that of the earth, with your head to the north, your root centre and feet pointing to the south.
5. Breathe rhythmically, allowing your magnetic field to benefit from that of the earth as it magnetises you and energises you, clearing confusions and congestions in your solar plexus centre. Imagine your own field merging with that of the earth.
6. You may do this for as long as you can, but at least five to ten minutes. Upon completion, briefly remember the wonderful clear light which radiates from your centre, through you and your auric field, making you a beautiful centre of light.
7. Ground yourself by focusing upon the contact between the soles of your feet and the floor, and when you are happy and comfortable with that, focus behind your eyes and open them as slowly as you can.

The basis of this exercise helped Mary considerably. She began to stabilise her energy levels, and she felt more in the centre of herself, less accident prone and altogether more powerful. The flow through her magnetic field was clearer and smoother than it had been, probably in her entire life.

Again, this is a very important exercise and ideally it should be repeated weekly, if not daily. It is wise to focus upon this idea at least briefly in a moment of pause, as often as you can, to reinforce the connection.

Not only is the magnetic intensity of the planet changing and weakening at this time, but the standing wave or resonance of the earth — the earth's electrical pulse known as the Schumann Resonance — is quickening, affecting us profoundly. This wave, also known as the base cellular frequency, was estimated to have resonated at 7.8Hz or cycles per second for most of this century, but has gradually risen since 1987 to over 8.6Hz. In as much as 7.8Hz is also the frequency our brain experiences when we are moving through the alpha waves of relaxation towards sleep, there are further interesting implications. There is some quickening taking place in the wave field of the planet and, to benefit from the natural nurturing electromagnetics and energies of our planet, we now have to align ourselves to it consciously, frequently.

In his book *Remote Viewing*, Tim Rifat mentions how Russian research also revealed that as individuals entered deepening relaxation, at 7.8Hz, their own electromagnetic fields merged with that of the earth, briefly seeming to disappear, and then re-emerging to be much bigger and stronger than before.

Perhaps this is why Mary benefited from the alignment exercise so much, as my vision suggested that she would.

As Above, So Below — As Within, So Without

Another significant problem in the human energy field at this time is that of energy freezing in the system, accumulating to cause the congestions and lack of movement, which result in physical disease.

There are many causes. At the emotional level, it is fear consequent upon ignorance, and we will look at that in more detail later, when we consider the astral/emotional body and aura. Even shock is really fear at the emotional level — fear of the unknown, the unexpected or the unrecognisable. Where we do not have a mental model for something and have not experienced it before, we are conditioned to fear it, and so our experience of it tends to reflect that; often we continue to fear it throughout our lives.

The energy body is no different when experiencing new frequencies and rhythms, and it will often lapse into a disrupted pattern, sometimes almost static, as the solar plexus — which is the primary magnetic and energetic chakra or centre — becomes confused and then panics.

One of the wonderful things about overcoming disease, at whatever level, is that the remedy is always close at hand. That is how nature and the universe works. And, in my experience, we often overlook the obvious in the quest for the amazing or the spectacular. Our need for a quest or pilgrimage is etched indelibly into us, and our path from disease to ease reflects that. Recognition of that idea is a part of the healing process.

Our contemporary obsession with cure — with immediate change — denies the journey we deeply desire to make. In our deeper, spiritual soul self, we perceive the journey as everything, with absolutely no sense of arrival to impede our growth and learning.

As a boy, in my summer shorts, I would often fall into a bed of nettles whilst in pursuit of a straying football or poorly aimed arrow from my home-made bow. The wonder of nature, however, provided, without fail, some neighbouring lush, green dock leaves, whose natural antihistamine, when rubbed upon the skin, would soothe away the irritating, painful rash that ensued.

Where there were nettles, there were always dock leaves. Where there is disease, there is always the remedy, and how often my boyhood green-stained knees would bear testimony to that. The cure for cancer is not in any rain forest, but wherever the cancer occurs.

There is always plenty — our whole notion of shortages is illusory, especially when it comes to energy.

In the ancient writings, and many global spiritual traditions that have come to us through channels such as Vedic teaching, Hermeticism, and indeed biblical exhortation, we have been given two very important, simple and connected ideas, central to our healing.

The first of these is the idea 'As above, so below.' The truth in this idea lies in the understanding of the greater, or the universal, and the smaller, or the individual, as essentially aspects of each other. The greater exists in the smaller and the smaller, potentially at least, encapsulates the greater.

A Reflection

Take a moment to consider this. It will not be alien to you as it is an essential desire in the human heart, and our higher desires are reflections of our universality, or, if you prefer, our innate godliness.

I am a great stargazer, and often, in all seasons, I will spend evening time gazing up at the stars. My sons, especially my younger one, John, will join me as I gaze up at the celestial carpet and marvel at the majesty of the Milky Way on a clear night. A few moments of open reflection upon the stars will stir in anyone a sense of belonging, a feeling of deep connection.

Reflect upon the universe and how remarkable it is. Allow yourself the thoughts from inside your heart — those upwelling, clear, open promptings that tell you how much you belong; how the greater is, somehow, a part of you; that the heavens above touch something precious in you. The heavens exist in you. As you observe them, they will begin to tell you how — you will feel the energy in you rise and rise, and your power will grow. Enjoy it.

As Within ...

Quantum mechanics has posed many a dilemma for us and for our scientific community. Not least of all, it offers us more control, or at least influence, over our reality than we were led to believe. Perhaps one of the most interesting aspects of this is in the disappearance of absolutes in how we understood our reality and the position of man as an observer in space/time, participating, often vainly, in the attempt to manage the circumstances he experiences in a somewhat embattled and victimised manner.

Figure 3.3: As above, so below. As within, so without

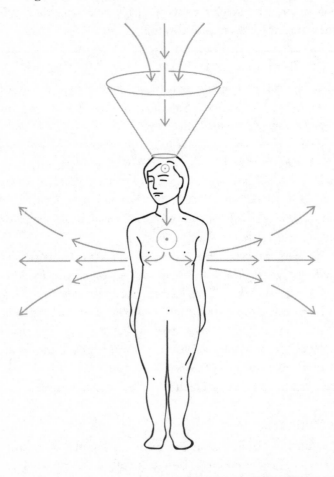

Quantum theory offers us alternatives. It reveals to us that there are not only different ways of viewing and perceiving things, but also, a variety of ways in which we can experience outcome to any given cause or course of actions. The sub-atomic particle is seen to modify its behaviour, dependent upon the observer and the gestalt in which the observer operates and thinks.

This is wonderfully liberating, and it brings the mystic and the physicist closer and closer together. It connects us irrevocably to our outer reality and gives to us power to affect our world, to change it and mould it, in keeping with our innermost thoughts and imaginings.

The true healer always seeks to attune to the highest (above) frequencies or ideals, to enable them to manifest here on earth (below) so that the greatest ideal we can aspire to (within) may manifest in our mind, body and circumstances (without).

This is the pattern of all healing, of all integration, and it is the manifestation of a great spiritual principle.

Exercise 6 — As Above, Below; As Within, Without
Stage 1
1. Sit quietly for a moment, and establish rhythmic breathing, as in the second part of Exercise 5. Enjoy the flow of power and light in you, as you relax more and more deeply.
2. Focus your attention upon the crown centre, imagining it as a wonderful vortex through which a glorious energy flows into you, touching every part of you, filling you with its power.
3. Here, the highest frequencies of the universe meet in you and become available to you in an unlimited flow of light, creativity and energy. The universe has unlimited energy — and you have access to it now.
4. Imagine your energy or etheric body — that remarkable envelope of forces, which releases vitality and power in an

unending, unlimited stream. See the energy strands on its surface, absorbing vitality from the vast sea of energy in which you exist. Feel that energy being drawn into your energy field and then into your physical body.

5. When you feel your energy level rising, something beautiful occurs, for not only are you absorbing energy, but you are now returning it by the same route out into life, to the planet, and out into the space around you. As you are nourished, so you return to life, in even greater abundance, that which you have received. You are becoming a universal processor and transmitter of energy.

6. Now, realise that you are breathing with the universe and you are breathing with the entirety of life — you are breathing through your entire body, energy flowing through the pores of your skin. Picture again the marvellous movements in you — from above to below, from within to without. You are the alchemist of Unlimited Universal Power and Energy.

7. When you feel that you wish to, bring your focus back to your solar plexus, and to your breathing. Your breath will have changed now, perhaps being a little more shallow. However it is, it is fine. Connect with the floor beneath your feet, grounding yourself in the earth. Then, slowly open your eyes and return gradually to normal awareness.

This process will continue in you, and the more you encourage it, the more the power will come and flow, promoting a wonderful healing.

Tom

Tom had been ill for some time and there were many contributing factors. He was physically a very big man; he had been a rugby player in his youth, but now he looked a weak, powerless giant. His aura patterns revealed some emotional

issues, not least the shock of his daughter's having been diagnosed with cancer.

However, his sustained high blood pressure had precipitated
a stroke, which had left him with a little residual difficulty in his
limb movement and some mental confusion. He also had a
'freezing' of energy movements, especially in his solar plexus,
which caused a general weakness and apparent lack of energy.

As is always the case in such disease, he actually had access to
lots of energy. By placing my hands close to his energy body,
sharp sparks of energy were released which felt like tiny electric
shocks. His system was literally crammed full with energy which
he was barely processing, and hence it was hardly flowing
through him. This was why he felt so weak and powerless.

It is important to note that no one is ever devoid of energy
so long as they breathe — it is impossible for it to be otherwise.
Our vitality simply becomes blocked and the ensuing congestion
causes tiredness, fatigue and the stop–start movement in our
solar plexus centre. Perceptions of limitation in us precipitate
tension and raised blood pressure. If we believe in limit, we
react as if it is true — our energy field obeys our thought and it
tightens, restricting the movement of vitalising energy.

To improve Tom's situation, the help I could give was essentially twofold. First, we had to do something to reconnect him
with his energy flow — to help him to understand the simple
mechanics of it and the limitless supply from which he could
benefit. We did this using the elementary breathing, thinking
and visualisation — as above so below, as within so without.
Secondly, by making my own healing attunement, I could help
stimulate and regulate that flow for him. He had to let go of his
daughter's situation and the emotional damage it was causing
him. He had to release the shock and develop some trust in the
scheme of things. For this, we also used flower essences, which
I shall mention later, as well as the realisation that just as there

was plenty of energy available to him, there was plenty for her also. But the real key was helping him to establish a sense of connection with Life, and the wonderful, inexhaustible flow of energy being offered to him by Life. This sense of connection was established, and his condition improved immensely as time went by. The last I heard, he had started swimming again!

Energy Banks

As you work through this book and its contents, there is a process taking place that is subtle, powerful and healing. I shall state often that awareness is important in healing and that it is pivotal in its unfoldment. Dis-ease flourishes in ignorance and the fear such ignorance may bring. Ease comes from under-standing. Each exercise helps you further along the road to ease, and changes you forever. There is no going back in healing. True, we sometimes slow down or perhaps become side-tracked, but with each instalment of knowledge and the growth in consciousness that ensues, we are changed and empowered.

At this point it is useful to consider one exciting aspect of healing and the creative process active within it. It is that of energy banks.

In my childhood, I was often puzzled by the 'clouds of vibrat-ing tapioca pudding' that floated around individuals, somehow quivering as an individual became more and more animated, and their thinking became more dramatic or intense. These clouds which varied in size and density, to a young boy resembled the rather unappetising dessert my mother sometimes made (another thing similar in appearance is frog spawn, which we also referred to as a synonym for the dreaded tapioca). In fact, the clouds are dense energy formations that drift close to us and to the earth, like silent, resonating dormant clouds of potential.

Figure 3.4: Energy banks

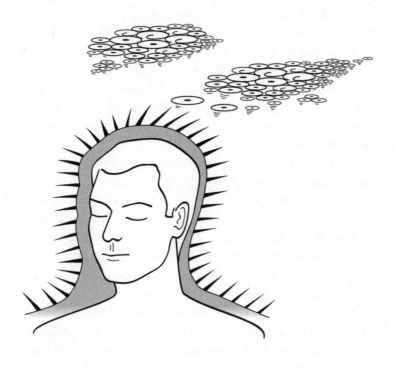

These energy formations may be considered as a type of invisible modelling putty, waiting to be attracted by the electricity of our thoughts, and then shaped into form in our three-dimensional reality. Upon closer inspection, I found the constituent parts of these clouds or banks to be small vortices of energy, the denser energy in the centre appearing slightly darker or heavier than the rest in its spiral. At this central point, the energy is vibrating close to the resonance at which it became matter. These energy banks are essentially neutral and totally available to create — in every subtle and intricate detail — according to the intelligence to which they are attracted. They are the perfect building material, the obedient servant of the conscious mind and the 'undifferen-tiated mind-stuff' of mental scientists and metaphysicians such as Ernest Holmes and the remarkable Thomas Troward. They are what the apostle, Paul, was referring to when he said, 'worlds were formed by the word of God. Things which are seen are not made of things which do appear.' (Hebrews 11:3)

From a healing perspective, these energy formations are very important, for they give to awakened individuals the opportunity to develop and re-shape their reality in keeping with their thoughts.

As we think, so these energy banks respond and are drawn to us, constructing form in response to the nature of our thoughts. It means we can build in our three-dimensional world as we choose. It is a knowledge of this feature of the energy plane that enables mystics to materialise objects, and mediums to bring 'apports' from higher realms. The thought transmitted with enough relaxed concentration and conviction will materialise here on earth in due course. This energy is subtle, and may be invisible, but is part of our three-dimensional plane, and of the same frequency as our energy body, and the vegetable, plant and tree kingdom uses these banks with far more ease than we do.

The implications for healing are enormous — hence the recent growth in visualisation as both a healing aid and a psychotherapeutic tool. There is a caveat here. Inconsistent thought processes and casual inaccurate image-building do not work well and, at best, produce slow, indirect results, which are, perhaps, not exactly what we might have wished or intended.

Consistent, trained effort will always bring response in kind. A practice of the following technique is worth every moment invested. It is another key exercise.

Exercise 7 — Using Energy Banks
1. 'Find the centre', as in Exercise 5, and relax deeply.

2. Bring your thoughts to your heart chakra and be aware of its sublime movement and function. Remember that the heart is the seat of understanding and, through the synthesis of the forces of love and wisdom, the heart will help you to unfold your highest desire and greatest good.

3. Lift your thoughts upwards towards your head, focusing first upon the pituitary gland in the centre of your brain (see Figure 3.5), symbolised as a circle. This is the master centre, which integrates and fuses together in your energy body the forces from all the chakras/centres which are beneath it.

Figure 3.5: Pineal and pituitary fusion and magnetism

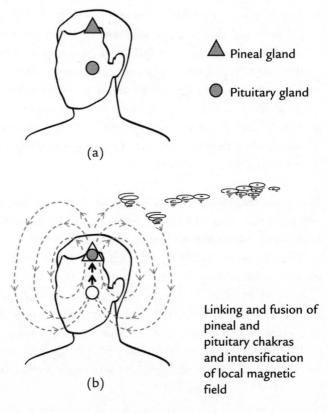

▲ Pineal gland

● Pituitary gland

(a)

(b)

Linking and fusion of pineal and pituitary chakras and intensification of local magnetic field

4. Imagine the pineal gland as if it is slightly above the pituitary gland, this time symbolised as a triangle.
5. Gradually allow the circle of the pituitary centre to rise slowly until it links with the pineal gland, eventually symbolised as a circle within the triangle. This creates a wonderful magnetic field in the head and a perfect space for thought forms to be imagined with intensity and clarity.
6. Encourage the formation in your imagination of an image of yourself in perfect health — happy, smiling and active. As with all exercises, clarity is important, and clarity comes with practice and patience. A few seconds of clarity are better than many minutes of confusion and vagueness.
7. Sense and imagine the energy banks around you — clouds of eagerly awaiting vortices of energy — being drawn towards the powerful electrical and magnetic thoughts you have created, energising them and turning them into substance — in this case, a powerful energy field and corresponding healthy physical body. You don't have to attend to each detail — the intelligence of the energy body will do that for you.
8. Finally, find the centre again briefly, and then connect with the earth through your feet, returning gently to normal consciousness.

This exercise, practised often, can bring enormous benefits and will precipitate considerable strengthening of the energy/etheric body and a subsequent healing in physical body cells.

It is possible to make this exercise more specific, and to allow the formation of images of healthy tissue replacing dis-eased tissue where you are aware of a problem. In such a detailed approach, it is important to have well-focused intention — in other words, to be clear which limb, organ or tissue is focused upon, and to build a strong image to accompany it. You do not, however, need a medical picture reference book for such activity. So long

as it is clear in your mind what it is you are seeking, your subconscious will help you to form the most appropriate image for
your task. It is useful, none the less, to understand the function
of the tissue you wish to regenerate and heal. If it is a kidney, for
example, ensure that you know the basic function of a kidney.
If it is a damaged joint, understand a little of its mechanics.

My own experience with clients suggests that the approach
in Exercise 7 is adequate for many people, and, with sustained
application, it can produce the desired transformation in any part
of the human anatomy. The more specific approach requires
more thorough and detailed imaging.

Be patient and don't be cross or angry with yourself if things
don't seem to work immediately. Remember, our healing is a
journey from dis-ease to ease, and such powerful techniques
may take some time and effort to master. But, from the moment
you begin, changes — however small they may be — will occur
within you. The universe with its vast reserves is on your side,
and there is plenty of energy to go around.

Moon, Water, Energy

*A young man once discussed with me the issues around my work
— spiritual ideas including the esoteric and astrology. He became
very agitated over the notion that planets, let alone stars, could
influence the human condition in any shape or form.*

*'I don't see the connection!' he exclaimed, thumping the table
next to him. He was a great blessing to me, for his challenge of my
views caused me to probe deeper into my own beliefs and understanding, and a little self-exploration under challenge is always good
for us.*

*I told him, the next time he was at the coast, to stand and watch
the tidal pulsing of the sea, and to reflect on how that movement
was primarily controlled by our earth's moon. Then I asked him to
remember that, biologically at least, he was mainly built from water,*

> *so perhaps the moon would have some effect upon the way he might feel from time to time and how he might subsequently behave.*
>
> *Consider this yourself — how the magnetic pull of our moon shifts the vast water of the oceans, and how our moon also affects our own feelings and power levels. In a sense, we are all 'lunatics', or at least influenced by the lunar phases and movements, and the magnetic tugs the moon makes upon us as our energy and our water are washed backwards and forwards. It is worth exploring the phases of the moon and observing the influence they may have upon your vitality and energy levels.*
>
> *Then, reflect upon the more immediate, more powerful, electromagnetic pulsing of your thoughts and the effects that that has upon your energy field and, in turn, your physical body. Think also of how you can create and build with the energy field and energy banks around you, with an effect in you more dramatic and powerful than that of the moon upon the waters.*

Waves and Radiations

Earlier, I mentioned the effects of the complex wave and electromagnetic fields we have around us and the possible ramifications for our physical (and emotional) health. I have observed these waves and radiations active in the energy fields of many individuals, and the effects they produce, both temporary and, possibly, permanent.

A businessman who travelled frequently and was keen to stay in touch with his office from around the world came to see me initially because he wanted some guidance and he knew of my aura and chakra analysis sessions. It was clear that he was very over-stressed, coping with life on a continuous and increasing energy deficit. Particularly disturbing for me was the fact that problems in both his energy/etheric body and his emotional field and aura were very evident.

At the energetic level, there was a noticeable depletion and flatness, predominantly on the left-hand side of his head, but also a little on the right. It was slight, but showed a reduced energy flow. In the short term, this would tend to produce muddled thinking, confusion, headaches and, possibly, problems in the alimentary canal and ears — affecting balance. In the emotional body, it would produce depression (see Chapter 4). In the long term, such depletion may cause permanent tissue damage, malformations, cysts and tumours.

He returned to see me for a second session and we were intending to focus upon some relaxation and stress management. As he settled down in my office, his mobile phone, which he had forgotten to switch off, rang noisily, and he answered it immediately with the kind of reflex action we all go into in such situations. Briefly, he forgot that he was with me. After a minute or so, he made his apologies to the caller, switched off the phone, and then requested my indulgence for his seeming rudeness.

I questioned him some more about his headaches. The rotations of his brow and eye chakras were both erratic, and were more so for the few seconds immediately after he had taken the phone call. Yes, he had headaches, he told me. And, lately, he often felt confused and muddled, and even dizzy. A blood pressure check by his GP had revealed nothing too worrying, but he had been advised to slow down, maybe play more golf!

It was quite clear that his mobile phone had become almost an appendage, spending many hours perched on his left ear. (He was left-handed and tended to hold the mobile in that hand most often, unless he had to write at the same time.) Viewing his magnetic field, I could see a slight twist in it as it passed his ear. This produced the dizziness he had experienced, the lack of equilibrium and the headaches.

Awareness Changes Everything

I mentioned to him his telephone and how I saw its constant use affecting him. Then, something quite remarkable happened. Just as the words had left my mouth, there was a very brief deterioration in the patterns and energy movements, followed quickly by a sustained improvement. The chakra/centre rotations became less erratic, the energy body around his head strengthened, and the magnetic flow in his aura opened out a little, becoming less irregular around the head.

Figure 3.6: Effect of mobile phone waves

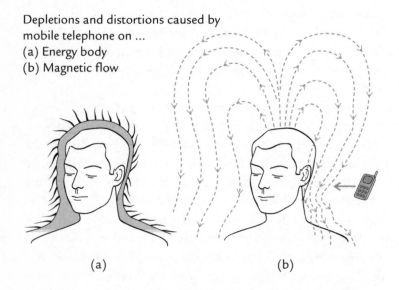

Depletions and distortions caused by
mobile telephone on ...
(a) Energy body
(b) Magnetic flow

(a)   (b)

This is a very important idea. It demonstrates how our awareness of a problem can, and usually does, precipitate a healing process in us, and especially in our energetic and electromagnetic pulses.

My client responded immediately. He said that he felt a little clearer, and that the headache that was 'humming away in the background most of the time' had lifted.

The improvement was not complete. I could still see a problem, though considerably reduced. We then set about using some meditational techniques to strengthen the movements in his etheric body and also in his magnetic field. We also looked at ways of making him less dependent on, or addicted to, his mobile phone. In so doing, we put him back in control — conscious control — of himself and his situation.

Mobile telephones and their network of masts radiate microwaves along with ELF (extra low frequency) signals. Such signals penetrate all energy fields and physical matter. If they didn't, the phones would not receive them, and the system would not work at all.

Various tests in the UK and the US have recorded damage to physical tissue of animals exposed to such phones and their waves, both when the phones were switched on and when they were switched off.

My vision and perception of energy fields suggest that we are only just beginning to understand the long-term significance of these waves and many others to which we are exposed.

It is certainly not necessary for us to cease using mobile phones or to be afraid of them. Even if we did stop using them, we would still be exposed to the radiations of the network itself and the many other waves and radiations around us. What is important is for us to be aware of what they do, because it is through such awareness that we change our relationship with them and take control of what is happening to us and through us.

The manufacturers of such items may not like it, but we should always consider the implications of the vast and increasing array of electromagnetic influences and waveforms to which we are subjected.

Computers

There are now, in addition to the earth's electromagnetic field and energy (ley) lines, so many wave and magnetic forms of man-made origin which affect our equilibrium.

Computers, in particular, emit very powerful waves, which may have a detrimental effect upon the energy body and especially the centres in the head and solar plexus area. This, in particular, can trigger depletion symptoms in the solar plexus centre, along with congestion in the head centres, especially the brow and the eyes. In such situations, we may become weakened and physically exhausted, and we may also develop migraine headaches, even mild fits, as well as tissue malformation. The screen radiations can also 'cook' the eyes and damage the retina, and computers should not, in my opinion, be used continually for hours on end, without a complete withdrawal for a while from the environment of the computer and the screen.

The complexity of computer and screen radiations is such that in one child I observed severe malfunction of the brow chakra, and solar plexus depletion of such severity that he had begun to be extremely anti-social in his behaviour, becoming excessively withdrawn. He also was losing some of his normal spatial coping mechanism and sometimes walked as if he were drunk with alcohol. Whilst it is an extreme case, as I have said, many ME and chronic fatigue cases I have examined have a 'computer' element in them.

The subtle radiations of a computer travel a wide distance in their dynamic and intense form. When in my back garden, I have unexpectedly felt and then seen the radiations from my computer as it is switched on by wife in my office at the front of my house, some forty or more feet away. I have no need to be afraid of this, but, again, I should be aware of it, as it is yet another phenomenon to which my energy field has to adjust, and it can take a long while — a lifetime in extreme situations

— to engage with this and the plethora of frequencies we are experiencing today.

Cast your mind back to your childhood and consider the increase in waves, radiations and subtle frequencies to which you have had to adjust, and you will have some idea of the confusion and stress with which your energy body has to cope, not to speak of higher bodies. We are fully capable of coping, for we are essentially and potentially very adaptable. But it has to be a conscious process.

Wiring Complexes

Complex wiring, both commercial and residential, can also be a problem and, again, a factor in the creation of energy-based disease such as fatigue, depression, exhaustion, wild vitality fluctuations, sleeplessness and, our old friend again — ME.

Every wire creates a magnetic wave or radiating field, very visible to the trained clairvoyant eye. When we place several of these together, we create very complex patterns of electromagnetic and subtle wave movement.

As these fields combine, a super charged field emerges — a kind of quantum, greater than the sum-total of the combined fields. It is very subtle and, as a non-scientist, I would imagine very hard to measure with instrumentation; in any case, instruments and meters can measure only what we design and programme them to measure. But I have seen several cases of depletion caused by these complex fields, especially in offices, call centres and the like.

Nuclear power stations can also pose a problem for us. The subtle 'low-level' radiations, both measured and unmeasured, are more insidious and deeper acting, and, to my vision, travel further than their more obvious brothers and sisters. At Sizewell, a power station on the Suffolk coast, the beach is in line with, but hundreds of feet away from, the power-station buildings and nuclear reactor. My wife and I could feel the waves from the reactor as we walked along the beach as many do each day. I often spoke of the mini-energy storm that I could see around the reactor building itself — like a subtle form of continuous lightning crackling away.

Figure 3.7: Complex wiring force field example

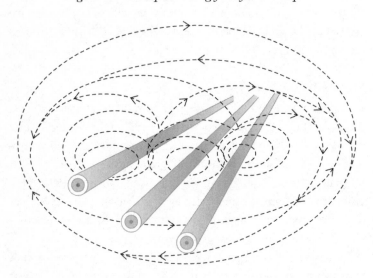

Again, we have to be aware, and we should be conscious, of all the gadgetry with which we have surrounded ourselves: TVs, radios, phones, fax machines, computers, fridges and freezers — in fact, anything that we have introduced into our homes or our worlds which adds to the electromagnetic spectrum around us, from electrical current, through radio waves, TV waves, microwaves, UV rays, X-rays and gamma rays.

However, we have no need to be afraid, and, by practising exercises such as those in this book (especially the earlier Exercise 5 and Exercise 8 below), we can make ourselves immune to the disruptive and potentially harmful effects of these intrusions. We have a remarkable, adaptable system, and our active conscious emerging relationship with our energy body can flourish in any situation, keeping us healthy and vital.

So, practise the following occasionally, and more frequently if you feel that you are exposed intensely to these radiations and waves.

Exercise 8 — Developing Radiation and Wave Tolerance and Immunity

It is my view that this exercise, coupled with an increasingly alert mind and awareness of the potential problem, is more effective than any gadget or crystal I have yet seen on the market.

1. Relax, and find the centre as in Exercise 5.
2. Visualise your etheric/energy body as a dynamic web of light. Imagine it to be wide and powerful, radiating evenly all around you.
3. Picture the energy strands on the perimeter of your etheric field, standing proudly as they exchange energy with the earth's own field.
4. Imagine your own perfect magnetic flow through your aura, with beautiful sweeping radiating curves flowing around you. The movement is untroubled and clear.
5. As you now radiate so much light around you in all directions, view yourself as in perfect balance. The sea of waves and radiations from all sources flows harmlessly around you, leaving you untouched, and you are now only enhanced by such encounters. Build this idea carefully.
6. Focus on the vortex in your solar plexus centre and see it spinning and turning beautifully, calmly, in a smooth spiralling motion.
7. Take your attention up to your brow centre and, again, see a calmly balanced, smooth movement as it turns and moves.

8. Through both vortices, beautiful clear energy flows in an uninterrupted and vitalising manner. You are in perfect flow, and your energy field is in perfect relationship with all the fields around it. It will remain so until the next time you link with it and pay attention to it.

9. Gradually, find the centre. Breathe slowly and deeply for a few moments before returning to normal consciousness, connecting yourself with the earth through your legs and feet as you do so.

Panic Attacks

It is appropriate here to consider the energetic nature of panic attacks.

As we grow, we become more sensitive, and our whole life pattern, with all its experiences, raises our frequencies. Each challenge we overcome, each problem we solve, each disease eased enhances the quality of our being, especially at the subtle levels, and enhances our capacity to function as a human being.

However, the increasing pace of modern living, along with energy depletion through electromagnetic changes as discussed, chemical pollution, dietary inadequacy and the de-humanising effect of our supposedly global society — which tends to marginalise the significance of the individual — all may contribute to an over-sensitive solar plexus and an auric field too responsive to the energies of others and the vibrations of the spaces around us.

Panic attacks are essentially our, usually temporary inability to cope with our rising sensitivity to the subtle vibrations around us — vibrations that are quite normal and manageable. When we enter a space, or encounter an individual, our solar plexus engages with them and makes an adjustment to their presence and their energy. If we are tired, or already a little anxious, we tend to experience further tension and fear until we become accustomed to that person, acclimatise, and thus feel more comfortable in their presence. We are all changing so rapidly these days that our personal encounters become more difficult, requiring greater levels of adjustment on our part, and groups of people, in particular, often take more energy to integrate and work with. So, we should feel something for public figures, teachers, entertainers and such people, for whom it is actually more difficult at the moment to do their work, and who expend more energy in so doing.

Our busier lives expose us to more and more people and we should recognise everyone we meet as a new energy centre, a fresh set of radiations to which we have to adjust and to which we can and will adjust.

A hundred years ago, even city dwellers often had a small circle of family and friends. Today, most of us travel widely and lead lives of intense and rapid interaction with many individuals. This requires more energy and, of course, greater adaptability. The same is true of situations. Most can recall when they have had their routine considerably changed — maybe starting a new job, in a different building and with a fresh batch of colleagues; or travelling somewhere different for the first time, using different trains, airports and so on.

Such experiences are stimulating, but they usually make us more tired than we would normally expect to be. The reason for this tiredness is the many adjustments our energy body, and solar plexus centre in particular, is having to make. It is working very hard indeed, assimilating the information from all the new energy fields around it, and making decisions for our safety and efficient experience of whatever situation or individual we are encountering. It is hardly surprising that, if we do not give ourselves proper time and space to integrate our changes, we occasionally experience exhaustion and the anxiety and panic which follow.

Furthermore, we may sometimes feel the vibrations and aura of buildings more powerfully than usual. And continued depletion leads to an overload, where the signals to our solar plexus chakra, its neighbouring nerve plexus, and also the heart centre are so intense that we do not always process them adequately and we enter into panic mode. We feel hemmed in, overloaded, and the solar plexus shuts down considerably to compensate for the depletion we feel and experience.

Here again, being aware of how the problem can occur is, in itself, the beginning of healing, the restoring of ease. Moreover, we have an opportunity to re-acquaint ourselves with our power and its flow through us, and so to make the most of our developing sensitivity. Instead of a problem, it becomes a wonderful asset. Properly managed, the phenomenon of the panic attack becomes a tool, and we can learn to benefit from a deepening awareness of ourselves, our world and the people who inhabit it.

At this time of increasingly sensitive solar plexi in all human beings, we in the west are doing our best to protect ourselves — with alcohol, tranquillizers and layers of food and fat. It doesn't work, of course, and eventually it makes the situation worse. The tranquillizers and psychoactive drugs temporarily numb our nerves, but fail to teach us how to manage the experience and energy movement. The food and booze chemicals simply confuse the issue, deplete and exhaust the pancreas and make the solar plexus work harder to keep pace with the effects of our extravagances.

When you have worked through all the key exercises in this chapter, and especially Exercise 8, you will have made progress already in managing any panic symptoms you may have experienced. Even just familiarising yourself with the principles will help. They may not be gone yet, but they will have been helped, as you gradually dilute their effects.

Managing Changing Situations

These times of great change are for us to encounter constructively. We cannot, and most probably should not, try to stop them, but rather, through our increased awareness, we should go with them as the powerful beings we really are.

There is one simple, beautiful exercise that you can learn and can switch on, quickly and frequently, which will help you to manage changing situations with ease. We cannot stop the magnetic changes and depletions — hence, for example, the need for us to use magnetic therapeutic devices sparingly, as we would use a crutch whilst a damaged limb repairs itself, or a sticking plaster to protect damaged and healing tissue. But we can adapt.

Exercise 9

1. Either before encountering, or when encountering, a new situation, recall the finding-the-centre exercise (Exercise 5) very briefly. There is no need to go through it slowly on this occasion — simply link with the idea. Even saying in your mind the words, 'I am in the centre.'
2. Think of the energy of the universe pouring through your crown chakra vortex as a bright, powerful beam, connecting you perfectly as it does so.
3. From your heart chakra, see radiations of silver light also glowing, helping you to understand and be comfortable in your new situation.
4. Imagine your solar plexus centre, radiating like a bright, yellow/gold sun, glowing magnificently in all directions.
5. Finally, a triangle of energy forms downwards from your solar plexus, through each leg to the soles of your feet and into the earth or floor, connecting your feet firmly to the ground. You are now centred and perfectly poised. You can be still and then move, as you choose, with ease.

I use this often, especially when travelling through busy airports and train stations. As with all the exercises, practise it often and you will be able to turn it on quickly, like flicking a switch brings light into a darkened room. The more you do it, the easier it becomes and the more powerful you will be, in any circumstance. And those around you will benefit too, feeling good and comfortable in your presence.

As we progress through our journey in this little book, everything necessary for complete healing will be shared with you. Remember at all times the considerable unlimited reserves of power that flow through you, each moment of your life. Recognise that, and make it real for you.

CHAPTER 4

THE DYNAMICS OF EMOTIONAL HEALING

There is an inmost centre in us all, where
truth abides in fullness…
And, to know, rather consists in opening out a way,
Whence the imprisoned splendour may escape,
Than in effecting entry for a light
Supposed to be without.

Robert Browning

I wanted to drop you a line to let you know how everybody got
on after the sessions for my parents and my son David. David's
knee made a remarkable swift recovery and he has full use back
of it. That is quite extraordinary, as he really had ripped it apart.
Thanks so much — he is cured. Also healed is my relationship
with him and his brother Thomas and, to a large degree, with
Susan (his mother). Very much also healed is my guilt from it
all — what a weight has been lifted from me! My father hasn't
looked better since any of us can remember. He's even talking of
moving to the West Country — not the words of a dying man.
He seems to see things in a different light — so positive. Perhaps
around now would be a good time to meet … I am now paint-
ing and perhaps a balancing up and some advice would be good
for me…. Thanks for healing my loved ones.

Simon's letter came as a result of substantial emotional healing
within himself and his family. The physical healing in his son

was, of course, important. He was in much pain and was very restricted by it. But the cleared emotional waves that subsequently flowed were far more important. For, had they been allowed to persist and gnaw away at Simon and his family, they might well have precipitated something far more serious and ingrained than the damaged knee and a little guilt.

Of course, I really healed no one here, flattering though his comments are. But I did participate in the process, being privileged to trigger off their own healing journeys, and helping to establish ease where disease had held sway: a father re-united with his rather estranged sons, and more at ease with their mother, his former partner; a wonderful beginning, that has already borne fruit as Simon helps his eldest son, in their new relationship, to establish himself in his education and make his way in life.

The light in Simon's emotional body and aura was beautifully clear and open, more than it had been for years. The rays, especially the violets and blues, which are connected with his creativity, self-expression and imagination, were particularly vibrant and even — how one would expect when significant emotional healing has taken place.

The Emotional/Astral Body

The Emotional Body is a remarkable aspect of human consciousness. Usually filled with gently pulsing and rotating streams of coloured light, it is the vehicle through which we develop our feelings and psychic nature, and emotionalise our thoughts. It makes us human, quite special as a species, yet also vulnerable. At its highest level, it reverberates with feelings of love and compassion, generosity and altruism. In this mode it leads us to love — to that sense of connection and belonging that we all need and desire.

The lower resonances of this body hold us in fear and separation, in loneliness and despair, and take us downwards into our anger and frustrations. Whilst all emotional bodies look different and there is, in truth, no such thing as a typical emotional or astral form, there are common features in most. Every one of us is different, unique, our aura and its energy and light systems reflecting this. But we also have much in common.

I should perhaps add that I am quite uncomfortable with stereotyping of any kind, and I have a particular aversion to books that suggest certain types of people are more prone to certain types of illness or disease than others. My experience suggests that we are a little more complex than such theories sometimes may suggest.

Whilst it is true that we have a genetic history, explained through miasms or hereditary tendencies, we also have many overlays in us, and certainly more than one miasm and genetic tendency. If we keep ourselves balanced, creative and growing, such structures will lose their significance and certainly won't limit us or define us. You are not a type. You are you, magnificent in your individuality. Thus any example is simply that — a guide to unfolding a principle.

An interesting example of an emotional/astral body was one I saw in a school teacher. He was married with a wife, three children, a dog, a mortgage and a love of beautiful things, especially art and music.

The colour distribution revealed much yellow light around the head, linking to his intellect, surrounded by the creative, expressive blue rays. There was a swathe of violet, the ray generally linked to the imagination, just beneath these colours, and then the greens of balance nestled in the centre. The lower half of his astral body was dominated by the orange light of vitality, resting on a layer of red — the ray of will, when under control, and frustration anger when not. These coloured lights are the reflection, in the emotional self, of their higher counterparts in the mental body.

All rays, their colours and meanings have an emotional covering. The colours are our mind's method of differentiating the various frequencies of light we perceive in our emotional bodies. This is the fourth dimensional self: the self in which we feel, in which we dream when we sleep and to which we retire when we leave this world in death or transition to the higher life. The astral body is a window — the window to our mind and soul. When it is clear, we think and feel clearly. When it is dull and patchy, our thoughts and feelings become clouded and dark.

In a normal resting state, our teacher's emotional aura was light and clear, the colours generally fairly bright. However, the introduction of his mobile phone had a remarkable effect upon the colours.

Simply by placing the phone closer to his head to observe the screen, there was a reaction. It was not in use, but switched on, and there was considerable disruption in the colours, with many small patches of red and orange light being drawn upwards into the top of his aura. This suggests some agitation in him, albeit subliminal, and such a sign is always indicative of imbalance and a need for healing around the head and shoulders, or wherever the patches are visible. For some it would appear, merely having a telephone around may raise anxiety levels and cause mild stress.

When the phone was activated by a call, his emotional field changed even more profoundly, drawing yet more energy and light from the bottom of the aura to the top. Such a movement is always indicative of excessive stress, and, if a long-term manifestation, more serious health problems may ensue.

When I observed this, the individual was not consciously aware of my observations, so the effects were not a consequence of suggestion or intervention. It was a simple view of the changes, and it surprised me considerably.

In this individual's case, protracted use of such equipment is, perhaps, not a good idea, although, when the call had ended, and I mentioned to him what I saw, there was an immediate and considerable improvement. The awareness of the problem had already stirred the subconscious into action and begun to put things right. Had the colours darkened and begun to show some patches of khaki or muddy brown in them, the individual would almost certainly have begun to experience some disorientation, mild depressions and possibly migraines. It would also stifle the action of the pituitary gland and the posterior lobe of the brain, causing emotional weakness and unpredictable, uncharacteristic behaviour patterns.

Just as these waves and frequencies were shown earlier to affect the flows of vitality in the human energy body, possibly causing some pathological changes, equally they disrupt the quality of the rays of light in the astral aura, with consequent emotional debility.

Again, I am not suggesting that we rid ourselves of mobile telephones. That is highly impractical, fear-driven, and unnecessary. But it does further confirm for me the emotional and subsequent energetic depletion we may all experience if we do not heed the challenges around us and develop an immunity to them. We are the generation exposed to these profound wave changes and increases, and are therefore charged with the responsibility of evolving and changing ourselves adequately so that we, and future generations, will be able to manage the new world environment safely and creatively.

In this case, some general work with chakras, as we have already considered, was useful, as also was some clearing of the emotional coloured rays, which we will look at further on in this chapter. The emotional body became brighter. The individual felt calm, relaxed and alert.

Emotional Pollution

Simon, writer of the earlier letter, saw enormous change in his emotional body as a result of the healing he experienced. Many of the rays became smoother, clearer, and less patchy. However, we live in a time of emotional flux and deep emotional pollution. It has been with us for centuries and has become a favourite tool of those who wish to control our lives.

Our advertisers constantly tell us that if we don't have certain cars, clothes, possessions or status, we are to be pitied and considered as desperately sad and inadequate people — emotional, as well as material, 'have-nots'.

This engenders in us an ever-increasing sense of dissatisfaction, sometimes hopelessness, and a fear of being 'left out' or 'left behind'. And so, we turn to many of the uppers and downers, pharmaceutical and otherwise, that temporarily anaesthetise us to our problems and our feelings.

And yet, this pollution masks the gloriousness of the human individual and the fine glowing feelings of which we are capable, and which I consider to be the norm. As soon as I remind a client of their potential and the splendour of the light in their emotional aura, so an immediate transformation and healing is begun. For truly healing and nurturing our emotional selves, there are some simple solutions close at hand. Our dear friends, the flowers, and the vegetable kingdom from which they come, are pivotal in this process.

Trees

'I think that I shall never see, a poem lovely as a tree' — so extolled the great bass singer, Paul Robeson, as I listened in my childhood to one of my mother's favourite voices. As a young boy, my natural vision of auras showed to me that trees, along with flowers and all vegetables, grass and greenery, radiated the most wonderful forces and exquisite rays of light, far beyond their physical boundaries — just as do animals and human beings.

Trees have their own energy or etheric bodies, absorbing, processing and releasing, throughout their lives, vast flows of energy from which everything around derives benefit. Perhaps more surprisingly, they also radiate coloured-light fields, which are their equivalent to our own emotional and mental bodies, so don't let anyone try to make you believe that a tree doesn't think and feel, because it does (see Figure 4.1). It may not have a nervous system such as we vertebrates do, but it is able to transmit powerful, emotional forces. What is more, the light and forces revealed in a tree's aura resonate closely with the higher, heart-based, aspects of our own emotional body, and they are able to help us as we seek to raise our feelings to higher levels and experience healing. Time spent with a tree is time well spent, and will certainly put you more at ease.

Figure 4.1: Energy and emotional field of a (beech) tree

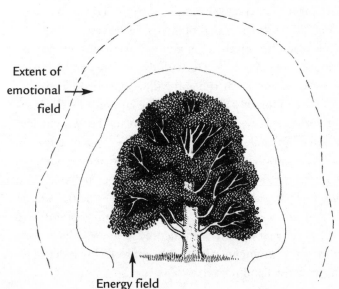

Extent of emotional field

Energy field

The Healing Trees

Whilst it is more convenient to do this exercise in warm summer weather when deciduous trees are heavily laden with their lush green leaves, it can be done at any time, in any season. It can also be practised in a direct or indirect way. Although this direct method — sitting close to the tree — is perhaps more immediately powerful, looking at one through a window, or even looking at a picture, will be effective, if a little slower at first.

Exercise 10

1. Find a tree, preferably one that you can sit close to, and which is in a quiet spot where you will not be disturbed. Some consider that certain trees are better than others for healing purposes, but my view is that different trees link with different people, although I would, perhaps, avoid a holly bush! See what you feel drawn to and trust your own intuition and guidance.
2. Observe the tree for a few moments. Look at how wonderful it is; it is a remarkable example of nature's diversity. Study it carefully — its trunk and branches, its leaves.
3. As you connect with the tree, you will feel your heart centre stirring and opening to it. Go with this feeling and let it happen — it will not harm you and will only be good for you.
4. Sit or lie comfortably close to the tree and breathe rhythmically and deeply as you learned to do in the last chapter. Consider the energy body of the tree — your imagination may even show you a picture of it — and sense your own energy body, in perfect rapport with that of the tree. You will actually breathe and energise together — the tree knows that you are there and will co-operate with you and help you. Let yourself breathe with the tree. Once you have done this for a few moments, you will begin to feel wonderful — more energised and relaxed.

5. Now, open your heart further. Seek to feel as the tree feels, allowing your emotional body to merge for a while with that of the tree. You will find this a remarkable experience. You may well cry — I often do in such moments.
6. Take a few more deep, rhythmic breaths, focusing upon your heart centre. Thank the tree for its help and then very slowly bring yourself back to normal awareness.

You will feel deep healing changes in your emotional self and possibly your physical self also. We do this often on my workshops — as my youngest son was heard to remark once, 'Mum, he's got them tree-hugging again!' The emotional healing such a connection may bring is, however, profound and may become permanent.

Spirituality, Vegetables and Flowers

Alice Bailey, the writer of a range of complex esoteric studies and books, wrote in *Esoteric Psychology*, 'The Vegetable Kingdom is the transmitter and transformer of the vital pranic (energy) fluid to other planetary life. A Divine Unique function. This fluid in its astral light form is the reflection of divine Akasha.'

Here, there is the allusion to a divine role for the vegetable kingdom, and its relationship to the astral/emotional body. Sometimes individuals have their mental state derided as being comparable to a vegetable (turnip in the case of a recent England football manager). I have always found such references to be, on the one hand, insulting, as intended, yet, on the other hand, also a back-handed compliment. For they connect to our highest emotional nature and our most elevated feelings.

Recently, a friend and client sent me some beautiful flowers as a thank you. Such a gift really opens out the heart and also lifts us up to our highest emotional experiences. So often, when we feel that we have hurt someone, or when they are unwell or just sad, we give them flowers to see and fruit to eat, that we may say sorry, or express our loving wishes and thoughts for them. We know that these gifts will make them feel better, and we have all been touched by such an experience at some time and have been deeply moved by it.

The progression towards vegetarianism in our diets is another aspect of our desire to clear our emotional selves. When we eat fruit and vegetables, we lighten ourselves, and the effects can be observed in the chakras in the astral body. The emotional centres are able to absorb light more easily and, as the emotional energy of the vegetable kingdom is so pure, the more contact we have with them the better — both internally and externally.

The vegetable kingdom is also more efficient than we are in other ways. Vegetables always produce more seeds than are necessary to continue their species, providing us with a wonderful, effortless example of the essential surplus and abundance in the world around us. And they do it without all the fuss we make and pollution we cause.

> *See the Lilies of the Field, they toil not, neither do they spin,*
> *yet Solomon in all his glory was not arrayed as one of these.*
>   Matthew, Ch. 6, vs. 25.

Astral, Emotional Man

As human beings, we are becoming more astral in our nature. The shift in us is away from three-dimensional awareness, towards a higher vision, where we are not simply aware of the physical realm, but more consciously active in a fourth and fifth dimensional world. This is why the desire to relate to our fourth dimensional self is now so important in our culture, as more and more people seek to understand the occult or hidden worlds of dreams, auras, chakras and energy systems and the spiritual life.

And, as this quest grows, so we become more active at that level of ourselves, in our astral bodies.

We are in rapidly quickening times. We encounter more situations, locations and human individuals than we have ever done in human history and in earlier incarnations or life times. Consequently, our relationships require so much more effort than in earlier times — marriages and partnerships come and go more often for many as we negotiate more and more emotional experiences in longer and longer lifetimes. My parents were married for fifty years and their circle of friends, colleagues and acquaintances was much smaller than mine. They travelled much less than I travel and came into contact with far fewer people and places, and thus had to encounter fewer emotional bodies and experiences. And my busy full life of many encounters is by no means exceptional or unusual in today's world.

So, thank God for the vegetable kingdom and the beautiful flowers they give to us. Whilst nature has its imperfections, we never see flowers at war, arguing or stealing. We need some of that light they bring to us, although we do our best to dig them up, concrete them over and wrap ourselves in a sea of tarmac and concrete, away from the natural world that can heal us and certainly help to clear our emotional bodies.

However, there is hope. We all have gardens, or parks and open spaces near to us. Garden centres selling their range of the ordinary and exotic plants are experiencing an amazing renaissance as, once again, we are driven to nurture our astral selves and avail ourselves of the healing light of nature. It is far and away the best way to heal our emotions.

Exercise 11 — Flowers and Vegetables

(A)

1. Take a few moments to sit amongst some flowers. If it is the spring, summer or autumn, this will be fairly easy for you. In

the wintertime, you may have to use your imagination — a picture, perhaps, or look at your indoor plants and flowers.

2. Study them for a moment. Think of the remarkable cycle within them — how they emerge from a small seed or bulb, grow beautifully and give of their splendour to all around them. Then they fade and die down, to return quietly to the earth from which they have grown. How easily they let go — and how easily they can help us to do the same.

3. Observe their colours, the subtle tones and shades of light they reflect back to us from the spectrum as the sun's light touches them.

4. Focus your attention in your heart chakra and let the flowers talk to you in a beautiful, silent dialogue.

5. Finally, return slowly to normal awareness, thanking the flowers for their wonderful display and radiation — they also heal through radiation, just as we are able to do.

As I have said, if you don't have access to flowers at this moment, find some beautiful pictures and let them speak to you. They will do so.

(B)
Repeat this exercise for fruit and vegetables. I remember how, when I was a young boy, the greengrocer's stall on the market always looked so wonderful, so inviting, covered in fresh fruits and vegetables. It was mouth-watering, inspiring, magical — and really luscious.

1. Focus your attention upon a beautiful bowl of fruit or some fresh vegetables. You may be about to cook them or use them in a meal. Just appreciate them and attune to them as you did with the flowers.

2. Remember the wonderful cycle of life in them, and how they grow. These fruits and vegetables also have a beautiful,

coloured astral aura radiating from them — if you attune deeply, you may even see one.

3. As you make your connection, so the astral colours around the fruits and vegetables grow and expand, offering more clear, emotional energy to you should you then eat them. They become more conscious of you, as you become more conscious of them. This is one good reason why we should say grace before a meal or bless our food before eating it. Kirlian energy photographs of food have demonstrated clearly how the auric field of food expands as it is blessed in such a way.

4. Study the colours — they reflect the colours they show to us for a reason.

5. Give thanks to the vegetables, bless them and return to normal awareness. When you eat a piece of fruit or a vegetable, or indeed any food, bless it, give thanks for it, and as you eat it, remember the source from which it comes. Remember also the wonderful energy it is giving to you as you eat it — you will get so much more energy from your food in this way.

Healing Flowers

Flowers have been used in herbal medicine for generations. They have long been known for their healing powers. The Cone Flower (Echinacea) of the Native Americans is now found in many households, considered a useful tool in the balancing of the immune system, and the warding off of virus and infections.

Over seventy years ago, the English doctor and homoeopath, Dr Edward Bach, identified how the light of flowers had a direct relationship to the human emotional body. He linked intuitively to the emotional field of certain plants and flowers so that they communicated to him the particular emotional conditions they could heal. In this process, he exposed his own astral aura to the information reflected in the astral bodies of the flowers, and found a whole series of correspondences, which were then captured from the emotional field of the flower into spring water — itself a wonderful conductor of energy and emotional forces. Thus, the famous Bach Flower Remedies were born, and they have been often imitated, but seldom equalled, as the light or aura around the stock bottles reveals.

It has long intrigued me how nature uses colour. I would often suggest to a client that they should include a high quota of vegetables or fruits reflecting a particular coloured light, as their astral aura indicated that a ray especially needed some clearing and healing.

A few years ago, I experienced a remarkable sequence of dreams. These were clear, dynamic and extremely compelling dreams, given like a set of instructions. I was told how the flowers around us reflect light of such wonderful intensity and high frequency — the highest in the physical world — that they offer to us an opportunity for profound, emotional healing.

The dreams explained how it is possible to capture these reflected colours, and use them to clear and heal the coloured rays of the astral/emotional bodies, healing our emotions and feelings. When taken by a patient in the form of an essence, the rays in the human astral body would seek to imitate the high resonance of the flowers' colours, raising consciousness and releasing destructive emotions.

I have never been completely happy with the various forms of colour healing I have met in my research, although I had also grown to realise that colour and sound bless us with the best ways of healing the emotional self, and there is no higher colour than that which the purest nature can give. Furthermore, because of the powerful interaction of the individual human emotional body with the emotional field of the earth itself, it would seem most appropriate that the earth should nurture the source of our emotional healing.

Flower Chromatics

As a consequence, and using my experience of viewing and drawing thousands of auras over many years, I set about capturing the coloured light from selected flowers in suspension, so that they could be specifically connected to the coloured rays in the astral body. It was quite difficult, in as much as I had to blend the flower petals carefully, matching as precisely as possible the colours of the aura and each coloured ray's band-width of vibration. This can only be done intuitively.

Gradually, I was able to produce a series of essences that resonate closely to the astral light, based on the chromatic or scale of colour. When applied, these have some wonderful results, which I will share in the following pages.

The coloured light of chromatic essences gives to us another approach in emotional healing, which complements happily all others. Instead of examining the emotional state of the individual, we explore the colour values in the emotional aura and chakras; this is something which anyone can learn to do. Then we apply the appropriate ray colour and the effects are often remarkable, clearing emotional problems and raising the vibration of the individual's emotional field in the specific ray.

Such an approach bypasses the need to explore every emotional issue — a task which is almost impossible in this lifetime — but instead provides insight and healing, often via dreams or by observing the changes in feeling and mood experienced by the individual. In these pages an introduction to the approach is offered, with other complementary techniques for cases where the essences cannot be obtained.

Exercise 12 — Garden of Light

For a moment, we are going back to our beautiful flowers. If you are reading this on a warm, sunny summer's day, or at a time when you have access to a beautiful garden, sit somewhere comfortable and peaceful. Otherwise, find some pictures of beautiful gardens or flowers from a seed catalogue or illustrated garden book, and study these for a few moments.

1. Observe the beautiful light of the flowers again — note the diversity of colours, and the shades and tones within each one. Consider what a remarkable tapestry you share your life with. Remember that everything you see is light — everything you feel, touch, hear and smell. All is light and the flowers reflect it so perfectly.
2. Close your eyes and breathe rhythmically for a few moments, allowing your breath to flow gently in and out of your body.
3. Now focus your attention inside your head, where you have your inner picture screen, and your imagination will build for you whatever you wish.
4. Before you, imagine a tall garden wall, and along it you can see a large wooden door, slightly ajar, waiting to be opened. Sense the stillness around you and the wonderful anticipation of what the door will reveal as you open it.
5. Open the door slowly. Behind it is revealed a bright, colourful garden — a garden totally alive with indescribable vibrancy. Trees, flowers and shrubs of every kind are to be found there, along with an abundance of magical birds, butterflies and everything that nature provides to make this a truly enchanted place. It is your Garden of Light — you can have everything and anything you wish in this sacred place. And flowers of every colour are there for you.
6. There is a quiet corner here where you can sit, observe and absorb the magic. Go there, rest and look at the flowers — red, orange, yellow, green, blue, turquoise, rose pink, peach, purple, violet, silver and white, and more. Note particularly the brilliance of the coloured rays each flower reflects. Note

them one at a time, savouring each moment as you do so, briefly merging with the flowers and their light. Enjoy it and fix the colours in your mind.

7. Take a deep breath and look around your garden again, watching the butterflies dance from flower to flower, before making your way back to the doorway. Step through, closing the door behind you gently.

8. Slowly clear your screen and bring yourself back to normal awareness.

You now have a garden to which you may return often, so that you can connect quickly and powerfully with the reflected rays of flowers. Practise it often. It will be a healing experience for you, and your awareness of the colours will grow.

The Ray Colours and Emotional Dis-Ease

During consultations, I often notice how a particular colour in an astral body reveals a problem because of its distribution in the aura, its texture or interaction with the other coloured rays. Let us take a look at some of the more common phenomena — as they affect each ray, and how they may express themselves in the way we feel and behave.

The White Ray

Many people, when elaborating on the use of colour in healing, suggest that all we need to do is to work with the white ray as that covers all options; early on in my work, I used to think much the same.

All flower-based essences work very quickly on the emotional body — sometimes the effects are easy for us to recognise, but just as often, weeks and months may pass before the improvements in our feelings become clear. The gentle ripples running through the colours of the emotional aura, indicative of the healing action of an essence within the individual, can be observed by the good, trained clairvoyant. They are reminiscent of the gentle ripples we see in a pool after a small pebble has been dropped into it.

The white ray touches all the rays and, as we need healing in every level of our feelings, of course that is most useful. It is especially useful in crisis as I said earlier, and also during an apparent set-back or shock. But the aura responds much more dynamically to the specific ray when administered and absorbed, sometimes after the white ray has been used and worked with first.

Eventually, as we grow close to perfection, we will resonate with a white, then gold/white astral and mental aura, but I haven't seen that yet, despite viewing thousands of auras in my work each year.

A clear white light in the aura is rare to view in large quantity and, when present, is seldom, if ever 'patchy'.

Ripples and Bars

A common phenomenon in the astral body is the deep-fixed ripple effect, usually across several colours at the same time. This mostly runs from top to bottom of the oval form in less severe cases, creating the effect of an aura within an aura, like a fold in the astral colours that runs around the physical and energy bodies. It rarely forms a complete oval, but does often run around the aura on more than one side of the physical body.

It sometimes indicates a period when the individual feels generally vulnerable, maybe excessively tired or emotionally run down. It also occurs when the individual is in a period of considerable transition, sometimes spanning several years, and it appears to provide an additional layer of emotional filtering of the signals travelling through the auric emotional field to the individual, somehow reducing their impact.

A German client of mine, Barbel, who is a psychotherapist and whose work was going through considerable change, recently brought to one session the aura sketches I had done for her over some six or seven sessions. We spread them out across the floor to view them. It was fascinating for us to observe how the pattern of colours in her aura had developed, and especially how a permanent fixed ripple of light had formed, held for a while, and then gradually had begun to fade. The ripple was at its most obvious over a period of two-and-a-half to three years, reflected in five of the sketches.

It is not a protection. Ideas of protection are fear-driven, harmful and restrict the aura's effectiveness, and consequently the ability of the individual to interact with the emotional space around them, and that of other individuals. 'Finding the Centre' and the light radiation are perfect in place of protection exercises (see Exercise 5). These bands or ripples are built by our consciousness when our sensitivity is exceptionally high, and especially during periods of transition, when our sensitivity is sharp and feelings are often in flux.

Healing Action 1
In such a situation, working with the White Essence and White Ray will help enormously, as a first step — indeed, it may be all that is necessary. However, in more serious cases — where more than one ripple has formed, with long, wide strips of colour, usually red/brown and black in appearance, running both later-ally across the aura and vertically, from top to bottom — a more detailed and systematic approach to the use of the rays is necessary, usually commencing with the purple/violets and reds, working then through the sequence deduced by the sufferer or the therapist, as I will show now in the prescribing exercises. It is also very likely that some work on the Five Cranial Energy Plates will be needed. This will be considered in Chapter 7.

ıth heavily barred auras feel imprisoned, cut off from ~~ıne, a~~ y become very isolated emotionally, unable to make meaningful contact with other people, or to sustain a normal life without considerable help.

Fig 4.2: Patches in astral aura

(a) Small patches

(b) Large patches

Patches

Uneven areas of light in an emotional/astral body are usually referred to as patches or patching. It is usually a deficiency of light, where the colour dims or fades as the individual struggles to express the highest, most wonderful quality in that level of themselves. Some colours seem to show this more than others, and we will now consider each ray, the effects of such a phenomenon, and modes of healing.

The Yellow Ray

In the yellow ray, patching is not uncommon, and its thin and inadequate presence indicates how such an individual's thought processes fluctuate or swing, in equal measure to the degree of surface imbalance. The greater the contrast in the colour, the greater will be the swings in the individual's mood pattern. Where the patches are dense and tightly clustered, the changes in feeling experienced by the individual will be frequent. If the patches are fewer, but broader, the mood swings will be longer and more chronic.

A yellow full of patches reflects as an individual full of mental confusion, and significantly lacking in confidence, assuredness and a sense of control. It is, perhaps, interesting to note that such irregularities in the aura are not healed by psychoactive pharmaceutical drugs. They are sometimes frozen or temporarily inhibited from worsening, but long-term use can sometimes make the patches sharpen and increase in size or profusion.

In such a mode we are very indecisive, prevaricating over the smallest issues, and usually experiencing anxiety states with a corresponding depletion in the solar plexus chakra. All the major chakras will be low in the absorption of yellow light throughout the astral body.

If the patches remain creamy in colour, the condition is not too serious, and it is usually healed through a period of rest and an opportunity to re-focus, change lifestyle and maybe career or job. If the patches darken and begin to absorb red or vermilion light into them, the emotional tensions become much more entrenched and fixed, and require deeper long-term healing.

One key symptom pattern in yellow patchiness is an inability to focus for long on anything, and a tendency to be generally ill at ease, and anxious much of the time. Since the yellow ray has connections with logical, structural thinking, we will experience uncharacteristic, muddled thinking when this ray is patchy.

Healing Action 2
First recourse would be to take two drops of the Yellow Chromatic Flower Essence, in water, twice daily.

The second part of the healing is to co-operate with the process consciously as follows:

1. Find your centre, as in Exercise 5.
2. Either sit close to some yellow flowers in your garden or open space, or enter your 'Garden of Light', sitting close to the beds of beautiful, yellow blooms found there.
3. Breathe deeply and slowly, imagining the light from the flowers flowing into your astral aura as you inhale, smoothing the yellow light beautifully until that ray in your aura is clear, bright and even. Eventually, you will feel the difference as you practise this exercise. Be patient and persistent. The changes that come can be permanent.
4. Give thanks for the healing that has taken place and slowly return to normal consciousness.

Pete, a client from London who was very confused and having many problems with anxiety, lack of confidence and consequent anger and frustration with the sense of inadequacy he felt, responded quickly to the Yellow Essence and the yellow ray. At first, he perceived only slight improvement, and requested that we should consider working with a different ray. However, his wife, who was with us at the time, told another story. 'You have changed so much,' she intervened as we spoke. 'The difference is amazing — you're much more pleasant, relaxed and at ease. You can't see it yet, but I can.'

The yellow patches in his aura were also less distinct and were responding well to the light of the yellow rays that the flowers were providing. He would later need to work on other rays, but his initial progress was indeed very heartening. He was able to think and act more clearly and more confidently as that part of his emotional body healed.

Also, during this period of healing with the yellow ray,

1. Take some long walks in the countryside or a park if possible. Try to remain aware of how the yellow ray is healing you, each and every day.
2. Try to deal with one thing at a time.
3. Give your mind some structured exercise, like playing chess or doing simple mental arithmetic instead of using a calculator all the time.
4. Keep lists of what you have to do, and work through them as effectively as you can. It doesn't matter if you don't do everything, so long as you see progress.

The Blue Ray

When patches exist in the blue ray of the astral body, several symptoms can present. One of the most common signs is, again, anxiety, usually manifesting through poor communications, with the individual being afraid or anxious about saying what they think or expressing their own ideas. It can equally be that the individual is too voluble at times, over keen to inform others, talkative but unwilling to listen. Creative, idealistic people who feel unfulfilled or devoid of ideas are often experiencing uneven manifestation of blue light in their astral body, and they are unable to connect with the most elevated thought forms in the blue ray.

Again, the patches indicate an uneven expression, so the conditions will fluctuate dependent upon the depth and frequency of the patches.

Generally with the blue patches, we are looking at our mental and, especially, verbal contact with others, and its balance, and also at our access to ideas which can fuel our creativity and help us to express ourselves.

Another feature of blue imbalance is our relationship to our peers. If we cannot live without socialising — being the type of social animal who needs others to validate them continually — then the blue ray, along with its orange counterbalance, is indicated. However, withdrawal and a tendency for unhealthy isolation are also consequences of irregular blue light, usually at the dark end of the ray spectrum.

Healing Action 3

As with the yellow ray, except using the Blue Chromatic Essence and connecting with blue flowers. Also, observe the changes you experience in your mental contact with others, particularly how you talk, listen and engage in dialogue with them. Especially practise listening

Remember how creative you are, that the blue light is always full, brimming with good ideas. Clearing this ray will help you to regain good access to them.

The blue rays are very auditory. They respond quickest of all the rays to sound, so listen to beautiful music often, sing and play an instrument if you are able to do so — get out that old violin or guitar that has been hidden in the cupboard and give it an airing.

The Violet Ray

Unevenness in the violet ray is usually found in imaginative individuals who experience mood swings that are quite obvious to those around them. They can, at times, be very imaginative people, with a positive vision of life and themselves, only to switch, often quickly, to a negative view, full of self-criticism, and they may become flat, devoid of vision at all, with an accompanying empty, hollow feeling. On a good day, these people can conquer the world; on a bad day, their depression is like a contagion, quite discernible, as the vision of what is possible in life, how good life can be, seems so remote from their experience. They often suffer with migraines, especially when under pressure or exhausted.

These individuals are also of the artistic type, usually with a keen sense or interest in colour, but suffering from artistic fatigue. Those who have a great fear of death may come into this category, along with those who have been abused, physically, emotionally and mentally, and retain strong memories of that experience.

Anna is a woman in late middle age, living in Munich in the beautiful Bavarian region of Germany. She had suffered from depression since she was a child when her father abused her, mentally and physically, and she was frequently disabled by migraine headaches. Her violet ray was patchy and she also had a little of the bar-like formation in her aura, which indicated a long-term, well-established pattern. She had a very poor self-image, usual in such circumstances.

I placed her on the Violet/Purple Essence and focused her in that ray, expecting a gradual improvement. The effect was immediate, relieving the migraines and lifting the depression significantly. Both she and her friends were astounded — and even I was delightfully surprised by the speed of the healing. She also began experiencing lucid dream patterns (since we dream in our astral/emotional body whilst asleep, such a reaction to Flower Colours is common), which seemed to be releasing old information and feelings. She said that the dreams were very healing, sometimes featuring her father, and she always felt bright the morning after such night-time experiences.

I saw her recently at a workshop of mine in Munich, and the improvements and healing are continuing — I've never seen her smile as much as she does now. The next port of call for her is the rose ray, which also had disruptions and unevenness in it.

Healing Action 4
As with the yellow ray, except use Violet Essence and connect with the light of violet flowers. Notice how constructive your best visions are, how clearly you can build pictures of a wonderful, uplifting life for yourself and others. Enjoy the colours in life, especially in the natural world.

Begin to draw or paint, simply for the fun of it. Use colours, playing and experimenting with them as you did when a child. Read inspiring poetry and literature regularly, and enjoy the pictures painted in your mind. Make visits to art galleries and enjoy the open air and sunshine whenever you can.

The Orange Ray
Unevenness in the light of the orange ray is also extremely common. It is the second most disrupted frequency in the emotional body, after yellow.

Usually, when our orange ray is affected, we are experiencing relationship problems, or adjustments, which can be very deflating and troublesome. Intense contrasts in the ray reveal an individual who constantly seeks approval from others, may be promiscuous, and finds stable emotions, and so stable relationships, difficult to sustain.

One woman came to see me with enormous problems within this ray and her red ray. Her ray was a deep orange, but with pale, light patches in it. But she also had a very sensual, red/aubergine ray, creating in her the need for a tactile, deeply physical relationship. The orange patches made that difficult to find in just one relationship and she was very distressed indeed, almost suicidal.

Good counselling had helped a little, but she still had real problems and was experiencing guilt and regret over her lifestyle and the many men, especially the good ones, who had come into her life and then departed.

I gave her some White Ray Chromatic Essence to smooth through the astral body, touching every ray as it does — white containing, of course, the vibration of all colours. Then, to make the healing more dynamic, I gave her the orange ray and the red ray to work with as I have suggested here. The improvement was gradual but effective, bringing greater stability over several months and, for the first time for years, with a sense of emotional freedom and clarity. She no longer felt that she had to prove herself, especially when meeting members of the opposite sex for the first time. She was more at ease and relaxed in the power the orange ray gave to her.

Menopause often produces problems in the orange ray and its complementary counterpart, the blue. A very gifted woman was experiencing some common symptoms of menopause — hot flushes, emotional fragility and tiredness. She was a psychotherapist, using her blue rays often both to hear and guide others, whilst, as is often the case, having to manage, but sometimes neglecting, her own pressing issues.

The orange essence, followed by the blue, stopped the hot flushes almost completely, and her subsequent improved calmness was a great breakthrough for her, as she was able to follow her demanding vocation with more energy and confidence.

Healing Action 5
As with other rays, except using the Orange (mix) Essence
and ray. Whilst healing this ray in your emotional body, be especially aware of your physical interaction with others.

1. Give to your loved ones hugs and cuddles that are non-
   demanding, totally free.
2. If you are still involved in sexual activity with a partner,
   during the sexual act, be conscious of the essential sharing
   quality of the experience, and think of the joy in giving and
   receiving in such moments.
3. Notice also how you can use your power in a controlled way
   during your day. Imagine yourself to be like a tube of magic
   orange light. You squeeze the tube gently, and the light
   pours out into life slowly and evenly.
4. Be wise and yet generous with your power, as it is unlimited.
5. Consider taking up dancing, especially belly dancing, or try
   yoga. Yoga is especially good for the management of this ray.

The Red Ray

Dieter was a pleasant middle-aged man, with a young family. He
lived in a small town, near to Frankfurt-am-Main in Germany,
and worked as a mechanic. He had a very dominant wife who
sometimes insisted on coming to the sessions with him and would
ask all the questions on his behalf. Occasionally, when he could
get a word in, what he had to say revealed a very sensitive man
who cared deeply about many things, but who was seldom given
the chance to discuss them. His inner feelings were suppressed
and he looked forlorn and resigned.

In his aura, his red ray was very blotchy and thin, and he had
given up trying to focus his will. The rose ray in his aura was
also pale and thin, suggesting unresolved relationship issues with
those close to him, with whom he wished to have an open and

balanced exchange through his heart. He was also experiencing problems at work — not able to put his point of view clearly when there was a problem.

Working with the red ray began to liberate him as he became more purposeful, assertive, and he could express his will more effectively. The next time I saw him he came alone. 'I have asked my wife not to come, and if she would like, to have her own appointment now with you.' That was some change for him and his red ray was stronger, deeper and clearer and his rose a little brighter also. A man of small stature, he even looked a little taller!

Uneven red rays are always indicative of a suppressed or unmanaged will. If the red is patchy but deeply contrasting throughout, again we meet swings in mood, accompanied by aggressive outbursts which send the red ray zig-zagging up the aura. As the colour thickens, it changes to brown and then blackens, obscuring the light from the mind completely. Of course, corresponding weaknesses in other rays are also common in such situations, notably in the rose and the green, and they will probably need help also. But the red will usually be the starting point.

Angry, hate-filled people often need attention to the red ray, as do those who are resigned, have given up and seem, as my Gran used to say, to have 'had the stuffing knocked out of them', and have developed the 'doormat' syndrome, allowing other people to 'walk all over them', taking on the problems of others as if they were their own. In extreme cases, such people are particularly adept at playing the victim and may almost enjoy being wounded. One of the most damaged red rays I ever saw was in a young woman of twenty-six who suffered from the eating disorder, anorexia nervosa. She also had problems in other levels of her astral body, especially the orange ray, which had made her sexually manipulative. People with red-ray disruptions are often ungrounded and, in cases of severe depletion, maybe not interested in life any more. Alternatively, they may be too sensual and earthy, materialistic and prone to physical excess of many kinds.

Healing Action 6
As with the other rays, but use the Red Essence and red flowers. Also,

1. Go for long walks in the countryside or parks when possible, and take up some physical exercise, like a martial art, tai chi or similar.
2. Practise Transmutation. Find the centre as in Exercise 5, then imagine bringing the clear red light of the will slowly upwards from the root chakra centre into the heart centre, the colour gradually changing from red to a deep, rose pink as you do so. This rose ray then radiates beautifully in the heart chakra, framed in the emerald green of the heart.
3. Look for ways of doing a physical act of goodness — a 'good turn' — for another, preferably unsolicited.
4. Gardening is excellent for all rays, but for the red ray especially.

The Green Ray

Perhaps the last major colour patching is to be seen in the green ray of the astral body, expressing in us an immaturity and meanness, a fear that if we give something away, we will have nothing to replace it.

Our fear of change and new things emerges usually through the green ray, and the lack of love for life, and the subsequent generosity we need to connect effectively with others, is also revealed in this frequency. It could be said that every kind of emotional imbalance can be found in the green ray — not a very useful comment from a diagnostic point of view, I realise, but none the less it is true.

However, the keys are to be found in our unwillingness to grow, to change, to welcome the future, whilst being at ease in the moment.

The green light helps us to let go, to move on and to accept that the natural balancing intelligence of life can and will work for us if we allow it to. Patchy greens, especially the darker ones, produce envy, greed and a consequent deceitfulness — a desire to hide things.

A very experienced and gifted healer attended one of my courses at a time when difficulties with her husband were coming to a head. He had many problems, coming from a very troubled, dysfunctional family. As is often the case, he had married a therapist because he needed one!

At the end of the course, she broke down in tears and needed to be alone. We had been looking at the rays and prescribing essences during the day, and I had suggested the White Essence and ray as a first call, as I always do in extreme crisis and shock. Her husband had been violent towards her and she couldn't cope any more, yet she loved him still. The White Essence immediately stimulated gentle waves through her astral body, giving a gentle smoothing to all the rays.

A few days afterwards, I received an e-mail from her:

Hello Paul — Thanks so much for a fascinating and very exciting day last Saturday. Sorry I didn't thank you before leaving — once you'd been in and out of my shock patterns(!) I felt very tearful and wanted to process things alone. The White Essence is amazing, wonderful, brilliant stuff, so calming and lifting at once — like a deep sigh! — can I get a new one from you when I need to ?

Going on then to take the Green Essence and work with the green ray, she was able to make the necessary changes, enabling her to take more control of her life and her relationship. What was especially interesting was how her husband began to change towards her also. One marvellous effect when clearing our rays is that, of course, as we radiate them through our astral aura, any healing that occurs alters the quality of the space in which we both feel and respond. Subsequently, those around us feel it also, and they often react accordingly, especially those we are close to emotionally.

Healing Action 7
Work with the Green Essence as in the previous exercises, and with the green light of the flowers and trees. Also,

1. Think of yourself as a continually growing and evolving being, flowing through life on a wave of love and wisdom.
2. Look at your letting go — sort out those things you no longer need, and give them away. Clear out old cupboards, old clothes and those things you have kept for years in case they might be 'useful one day'! Make space for the new!
3. Work on the forgiveness exercise in the next chapter.
4. Make plans to initiate change in your life where it is needed and, especially, travel and visit new places and people.
5. Seek small ways to help others beyond the normal call of duty.
6. See yourself as a centre for giving and receiving.

The Rose Ray
The rose ray will show patches and unevenness when our capacity for intimacy and affection is damaged. Irrespective of the particular shade of rose visible, patches reveal inadequacy. Many large ones produce cold, distant relationships with others, often the consequence of being hurt or continually disappointed and let down, especially by partners, lovers or close members of our family and friends.

Small patches in a pale rose produce shyness and, if accompanied by tensions in the magnetic rhythms in the aura, as mentioned in Chapter 3, agoraphobic and anti-social behaviour may be exhibited, sometimes extreme in nature.

In my aura assessments, I often refer to 'cuddler's pink', a vibrant, deep rose light which indicates a truly affectionate, loving soul. Where the rose is patchy or extremely pale, we may be devoid of affection, neither giving nor receiving it adequately, or simply having grown up in a family where affection was not freely expressed and explored. Without a good rose ray, we are incapable of relaxed intimacy, and physical abuse may also show here, as well as in other rays — notably, orange, violet and sometimes yellow. Those who had domineering or, equally, weak parents will also have patches in this ray.

One young woman I knew well had problems in forming and sustaining relationships with young men, and she was a little in despair. She was attractive and intelligent, but had often been disappointed. I placed her on the White Essence first, followed by Rose. Within days, she attracted two new invitations from eligible young men, and was given a chance to work at relationships again. Whilst not perfect by any means, the partnership she subsequently enjoyed was one of the most successful partnerships of her life so far.

Healing Action 8
Take the Rose Flower Chromatic Essence and work with the rose-coloured flowers as in the previous exercises.

1. Be thankful for partnerships, friendships and family, and find ways to show how much you value them.
2. Be kind to others in small, but meaningful, ways.
3. Remember that if we open our hearts lovingly to others, eventually, in some way, somehow, that love will be returned.

A good rose ray also makes us more patient in our dealings with others, more accommodating and accepting of their idiosyncrasies.

Party Mix

During a training course I held in the UK for therapists wishing to work with the Rays and my Flower Chromatic Essences, I asked the students to use a particular mix of essences and rays upon themselves. Generally, I encourage working with the rays, and therefore the essences, one at a time, as it is simpler, and it is also easier to observe their application and effectiveness.

On the other hand, on a few occasions, I have used more than one ray at a time, especially blending white with colour. I also often use Rose and Silver rays together, as they frequently appear in close proximity to each other within the astral body or aura.

For this occasion, I asked the students to test a mix of white and a special pale turquoise/violet. It was essentially an intuitive decision on my part, but I was aware that this blend of rays produced an unusual resonance and vibratory field.

The effects were quite remarkable — one student, upon taking it, reported some of the best sleep he had experienced for years; and two others had interesting, similar experiences on the first evening. They each had to attend different social gatherings that evening and both encountered individuals with whom they had previously experienced difficulties. In one case, it was a considerable dislike, and in the other, a continual tension and unease in the other person's presence. Both reported how this had changed. They felt at ease — indeed, in one case, unusually open and relaxed in the situation, sitting next to the person at dinner. They also both reported how the other people appeared to be more at ease with them.

This case illustrates the powerful interactive principle in ray healing, and the effect of the essences in healing the light of the emotional body. As the students became more at ease with themselves, their own auras clearing of emotional tensions, so they had a dynamic effect upon the space around them and the individuals who came within its compass and influence. It is particularly interesting also because of its immediacy and the fact that it was essentially a blind trial — the nature of the rays in the essence being unknown to the students beforehand.

Of course, the effects were not the same for everyone in the group — such blanket prescribing could not be, as nothing is universally applicable. Our differences and uniqueness make that impossible. But it reinforces for me the importance and value of the therapeutic application of colour rays upon the emotional body in the quest for health, and the reflected light of flower colours in particular.

My experience suggests that it is by far the best way to heal the emotional or astral body and bring ease into its amazing light. One humorous member of the training group mooted the title 'party mix' for the essence — most appropriate in the circumstances!

What Colour?

There are many ways of deducing which ray colours are important for you to use in emotional healing. And remember that, as you work with the rays, the insights will come, articulating the healing process taking place within you. Sometimes, you will bring back memories from your dreams, and these will speak to you in your healing. Others will also notice — probably before you do — how you grow and heal.

The best approach for discovering which rays and ray sequence you should work with is the intuitive one. Unlike other methods, where an emotional/psychological profile is used, this method is, in my experience, far superior, and more in keeping with fourth and fifth dimensional consciousness of our emotional and mental selves, as it is possible and common for two people to display similar emotional symptoms for different reasons, and therefore a different sequence of rays is likely to be useful in each case. Furthermore, whilst some psychological correspondences are useful, as we have explored a little already in the phenomenon of patches in different rays, an intuitive colour assessment should be the primary source of diagnosis. The emotional clues are a cross-check once the ray has been ascertained by an intuitive method.

Using the methods in this book, you can work safely and harmlessly on yourself, and on others if you are a therapist. In everyone's astral body, all rays require some healing, continually, as we make our journey from dis-ease to ease, and free ourselves from the enormous emotional clouds that have gathered around our human family during thousands of years. It is a question of finding the pattern and sequence you can identify as most appropriate to work with.

Identifying Your Emotional Rays
Self-Prescribing
Exercise 13 (A) — Garden of Light
Visit your special, inner garden again.

1. This time, whilst you are there, resting in the quiet corner you have found, focus your attention in your heart centre — it will already be very open as the light of the flowers touches you.
2. Through your heart, see which colours attract you most, which colours have the greatest allure, making a note of the sequence revealed to you.
3. Return from your garden as before, and this time, find yourself some colouring pencils, or crayons, and paper. On your paper, celebrate your visit to your garden by drawing the

flowers in the colour sequence you experienced. Really enjoy this part of the exercise. Return to the uninhibited times in your childhood when drawing coloured pictures was fun. When I was teaching young children, it gave me great joy when my tiny pupils would come to my desk, beaming a smile from ear to ear, waving their drawings under my nose with pride and enthusiasm. It was a privilege and I was always delighted.

This is your sequence to work with, and, from time to time, you can return to your garden to see the next stage of your ray development and to experience the healing of the flowers whilst you are there.

One client, a retired teacher, found this approach the most useful one, and, over eighteen months, has successfully worked through a process which has seen her release many fears and anxieties, and also bring clarity into her relationships with others — particularly a poor mother–daughter one, which had troubled her for many years. Her working with the rose ray and essence in particular precipitated many breakthroughs, and they are now enjoying a new, open friendship.

A middle-aged Swiss woman, also using this simple diagnostic method, overcame her fear of travelling, and especially her anxiety when flying on long-haul flights. She would always be restless and anxious before and during such journeys. Since using the white and then green essences, she has made intercontinental flights to China and India in a relaxed and happy mode, even managing to have some good refreshing sleep — something she had never been able to do before. She coupled this with some practice of the magnetic pole and planetary alignment in Exercise 5.

Self-Prescribing
Exercise 13 (B) — Colour Strips
This is another good intuitive approach to self-prescribing.

1. Using some coloured pencils or crayons, make a colour strip. Start with the red, and work through the tones and shades, so that as many rays as possible are covered — reds, oranges, yellows, greens, blues, violets, rose, silver, peach and white.
2. Take a few rhythmic breaths and briefly find the centre, as in Exercise 5.
3. Place your index finger about an inch above the colours and, focusing your attention on your solar plexus centre, move it slowly along the lines. Note any tingling or change in sensation in your fingertip as you do so. Where the sensation is strongest, you are being told that that colour is important for you.
4. Make a note of which colours register most — there may be two or three.
5. Repeat the exercise with the colours you have selected, noting the differences. With practice, you will be able to work out a sequence of two or three rays that are important for you to work with.

Using a Pendulum
If you have a pendulum, and are practised at using one, you may use such a device in conjunction with your colour strip.

Hold the cord or line attached to your pendulum, allowing it to hang as still as possible. To use a pendulum for this purpose, you must make a statement to obtain an affirmative or negative response. You can discover very simply what movement your pendulum will make to say 'yes' or 'no' by making a sequence of statements, some of which you know to be true — 'My eyes are blue', 'My name is Paul', and so on — where the rotation or movement you see in your pendulum will be affirmative, and some statements you know are untrue — 'My grass is red', 'My name is Ozimandius, King of Kings!' — where the rotation will be different, being the negative or 'no'.

With a little practice, you will soon establish the way to read 'yes' or 'no' from your pendulum, and the method can become very reliable and accurate. When deducing which rays to treat first, use a statement such as: 'This ray colour is a priority now in my emotional healing' — whilst focusing upon that colour on your strip.

Before and after using a pendulum for any activity, do 'Find the Centre' to ensure clarity. The pendulum simply amplifies your own intuitive response to make it clearer for you — it has no power of its own, and the more relaxed and centred you are, the better it will work.

I use a metal pendulum sometimes, purely for teaching purposes, but use anything you are comfortable with — a piece of string and a pebble will do just as well. I always bless everything I use, including a pendulum, before I use it, as it places the item in the highest level of contact with you and your life, and is an honouring of the impeccable service it will give to you: 'I bless you and thank you for working with me to help me perfectly in unfolding my highest good.'

Self-Prescribing

Exercise 13 (C) — Colour Intensity

Equally, you can use your pendulum to read the colour intensity of the rays in relation to your need.

1. As you place a fingertip above each colour, hold the pendulum in your other hand, and simply allow the pendulum to rotate, slowly or quickly, as it chooses, in any direction. In your mind, place the thought that the faster and stronger the rotation, the more important the ray colour is in the healing of your emotional body.

2. Observe the rotations for each ray carefully, and you will detect two or three especially strong movements. You may be able to sequence them straight away, but, by a process of elimination, you will be able to decide which ray is important to heal first and what comes next.

The more you practise this, the better you will become at it. With all healing, patient persistence is the key, and the same applies to when we are deducing what course of action to take. In self-diagnosis, you will even begin to benefit from the healing effects of the rays as you make contact with them in these exercises.

In situations where it may still be a little unclear and you cannot decide between two or three rays (the likelihood is that they may all need some similar and significant degree of help), you can do the following:

1. Choose one of the rays and place your fingertip above it.
2. Close your eyes and first try to 'feel' the colour in your solar plexus chakra or centre. You may have a slight response here of attraction or rejection, warmth or cold.
3. Lift the colour into your heart centre and connect with your heart. Each ray will make your heart open, but the degree of expansiveness you feel will vary.
4. Bring your attention to the space in your head behind your brow centre and imagine the colour as clearly as you can.

Repeat this with each of the two or three selected rays, and the one that is easiest to see in your imagination — the brightest one — is the one to use first, followed by the next brightest and so on.

Flower Pictures
Another method for deduction, both for yourself and for patients, is to collect pictures of flowers, or even take photographs of

them yourself. For the green ray, whilst there are flowers with green light, such as lady's mantle, you can, of course, use leaves and foliage. You can then use the same approach as in the colour strips to determine which rays to use.

One client made a veritable scrapbook of photos and cuttings from garden catalogues as her prescribing tool. Others have found that, simply by placing their hands close to the flowers in their gardens in the spring and summer months, they can deduce which rays are important in their healing — the flowers will help you if you ask them.

Traffic Lights and Astral Aura Vision
These methods of seeing rays and colours are touched upon in my earlier book, *Auras & Colours* (Gateway, 2001), but they are important to mention again here.

Attunement to the astral body may already be a skill of yours, and you may be able to see the blemishes and patches in the rays as you tune into individuals. However, it takes some skill, practice and experience simply to view the astral body clearly enough to make a diagnosis based upon that vision, whether viewed subjectively within the imagination, or objectively around the physical body, and such is not the province of this book.

However, the traffic-light sequence I use to determine important ray significance for an individual is equally useful in a healing context, so it is repeated here.

Self-Prescribing
Exercise 13 (D) — Traffic Light
DIAGNOSIS

1. Find your centre and radiate your light.
2. Place in your mind the idea that the object of this exercise is to view the rays in your astral body that need healing most at this time. Remember that we find what we are looking for.

3. Imagine a set of blank traffic lights waiting to be illuminated in the colour sequence that you need to see.
4. Then, gradually, call up the first colour, allowing it to shine from the top of the traffic light.
5. Repeat this for two or three colours, lining up the colours one beneath the other, until the sequence is complete. Say 'thank you' — we should do this after everything and every exercise, as it is good and respectful and it also impresses the subconscious to continue the good work for us in the future.
6. Clear your picture, making a note of the colours, and find your centre briefly.

This approach can also be used by a therapist seeking to prescribe for another. Over the years, I have yet to find anyone, from the many people I have trained, who cannot develop the above technique for determining ray colour for all kinds of purposes — in this case, for healing the emotional self in the astral body.

Prescribing for Others
Exercise 13 (E)
(1) Aura Prescribing using Chromatic Essences
One of the best methods I have found for practitioners, and those seeking to help others in their healing process, is the following one. Usually, I prescribe using auric vision for my clients and patients, but this approach involves them more actively and can be extremely effective. For this, you need a set of my Chromatic Flower Essences or a bowl of coloured flower petals (in the summer months) or some coloured cards for each of the main rays.

1. Place your patient or client on a comfortable chair or couch. Help them to relax by asking them to focus upon their solar plexus centre and, as they breathe rhythmically, for a few moments, to slow their breath gently and gradually.

2. Once they have relaxed, standing slightly to one side of them, a few feet away, and outside their immediate aura, pick up either a bottle of flower essence or a coloured card or petals. For this to work, the petals must be monochromatic and not have mixed colours on them.

3. Very slowly, introduce the essence, the coloured card or petals through the client's aura, carrying it towards their body, level with the torso, somewhere between the heart and solar plexus centres.

4. Quietly tell your client what you are doing and ask them to 'feel' the ray as it enters their aura. The nature of the sensation they feel will vary, but generally they will be able to discern which ones affect them most powerfully. As the bottle or card enters the aura, they will connect with the light of that ray and sense the healing potential for them contained within it.

5. I usually find that one essence and ray colour stands out from the others with, perhaps, another one or two being a close second and third. The experience the client will have will usually be sentient — a feeling that a particular one is important and most healing for them. Some may actually have a visionary response and their imagination will show clearly and brightly the colour(s) that is (are) most important at that time. They may say, 'This makes me feel good, positive,' or 'I have no particular feeling with this one.' Sometimes, although rarely, they may sense a definite 'no' towards a ray.

(2) Aura Vision Method
If you have well-developed aura vision, you will be able to make diagnosis using this method.

1. Sit your patient so that you can view their astral aura comfortably, either using the subjective approach, where you

view their light bodies around their physical form, or the more common objective approach, where the image of their aura is shown inside your head on your inner picture screen. With the objective method, you can, of course, view your client's aura at a distance as well as when they are physically with you.

2. Relax and view their astral body — remember that you will be shown what you seek and what you ask your subconscious to reveal to you. With experience and practice, you will easily 'switch on' the picture you require.

3. When you have your vision, scan the aura slowly from top to bottom. The secret to doing this successfully is to imagine that you are, literally, a scanning machine, able to view slowly and accurately the whole emotional field. Regular practice of this will ultimately bring success.

Test for the following — bars and fixed ripples around the edge of the aura; patches of light; mixing, where patches of one colour seem trapped inside another; mist, usually red and orange; over-dominance of one particular ray in the aura.

If you find serious barring and fixed ripples or folds in the light of the astral body, the first action is to apply healing with the white ray. Such a soul will often display nervousness, sometimes extreme, be fidgety and, perhaps, depressed, linked with little sharp bursts of prickly anger. They may also be very defensive, inclined to fold their arms over their heart centre. In very serious cases, you may also perceive small barbs of red/black energy, moving a little menacingly around the aura, like missiles waiting to be aimed at the next available target. These are barbs of negatively charged energy, full of fear and anger. It may take intensive use of the white ray to clear this enough to work with the individual rays. Where the barbs are light, and maybe only partly to be seen, a small amount of white-ray treatment will work very quickly and deeply.

Clearing Patches

When the bars, ripples and folds are less distinct, you may begin working with the specific rays, more dynamically. For this, you should look at the patching, where the light is uneven. With in-depth investigation, you may find that there are patches in all or most of the rays. In such a situation, start with the colours at the top of the aura and work towards the bottom — as it appears at the initial diagnosis. As the rays and essences are used, so the aura will change, so go with this initial sequence to start with, whilst, at the same time, viewing the astral body regularly at each consultation to check what is happening. You may well find that as you work on a ray, so the effects on other rays will also be very positive, and you may then have to review your initial sequence. The secret is to have a strategy, but also to be flexible and adaptable as you progress and work through it.

Work with essences and rays through each colour until improvements can be seen in the astral aura and in the feelings and emotional condition of the patient. Remember here that, as the emotional body is being healed, you may well see physical changes occur, because the interaction between soul, mind and body becomes stronger and clearer.

Also, remember where using the essences that they are harmless but, on occasion, as with all healing, there will very possibly be a brief time of clearing. All healing works from inside to out, from top to bottom, so there can be some healing reactions. However, these are always slight and temporary where they occur, and the occasional very slight worsening of symptoms can be viewed as a positive sign that healing is occurring — again, very rare, but important to mention here.

When you have worked with a client or patient on two or three rays, you will probably find that a tendency for the red or orange mistiness to rise to the top has cleared, and the responses of the client are much improved. If however, the tendency is still there, work with that next.

Colour Mixes and Ray Dominance

Slightly more sophisticated is the approach to colour dominance and colour mixing in the astral body. Where this is evident, you treat the dominant ray. For example, we see a mix in the yellow ray, where the yellow ray has been infiltrated by orange. This is very common in a society where naked ambition and a disregard for the feelings of others are often applauded as determination and a part of the 'go for it' mentality which is so prevalent today. Such people can be ruthless, arrogant and often patronising — a pattern very common amongst politicians, some entertainers (especially those with little talent and big egos), and those of managerial class who feel they have a divine right to govern everyone else in autocratic style.

Here, we treat the yellow ray, so that it may be purified and cleared. The time this takes will vary from situation to situation, so, sensitive, perceptive monitoring is, of course, essential.

Another common mix is a red/brown in the violet ray, producing continual frustration and negative feelings when dreams and ideals seem hopeless and unattainable. Often you will hear from individuals with such a mix the words: 'It would be so wonderful, but life isn't like that', 'It can never be', or 'I never get any luck' — high thoughts and visions, destroyed by negative feelings of inadequacy and the willingness to be the victim, or the melancholic. Here again, the violet ray would be treated, before anything else, and the red/brown areas would dissolve, gradually, but surely.

Ray dominance is less easy to determine. Usually, obsessive behaviour in one particular area of life reveals a problem of this nature. But where more than 30 per cent of the field of the aura is covered by one ray over many weeks, it needs some help from the flowers and the rays they reflect.

Individuals still developing aura — and hence astral body — vision are, perhaps, best using the 'traffic light' method explained earlier, whilst their auric vision unfolds.

Tears, Rips, Cracks and Cameras

It is probably useful here for me to dispel a few myths and clarify one or two ideas.

First of all, I have over the years had many souls visit me because they feared they had tears, rips or cracks in their auras. Most language, when used to describe the wonderful and some-times challenging effects of the light we radiate, is hopelessly inadequate, but it is, at present at least, the best we have. Even my use of the terms 'patches', 'ripples' and 'bars' is inadequate terminology, which I use merely in an effort to describe light patterns in the aura.

Your aura cannot be torn, ripped or cracked, and it certainly doesn't need 'auric sticking and darning', which is one of the many idiotic three-dimensionally focused phrases and explanations I have heard. We are dealing with light which moves in waves and particles, and hence we use the essence of that light to bring balance and clarity into its nature — we heal like with like. You and your aura cannot be healed by some kind of cosmic super glue or psychic thread.

Also, it is worth mentioning the cameras and technology that appear to photograph auras. Whilst it is interesting, and a gifted psychic can make a fair assessment from what it records, I have examined many of these machines over the years, and, whatever they reveal, it is not the astral body. They may register changes, but inevitably they reflect the consciousness of both inventor and user, and, whilst there is obviously a degree of subjectivity in all these ideas, most good psychics agree that what they see in an astral body often bears little resemblance to the photographs, especially in relation to ray colour, distribution and texture. The fact that they can be 'read' accurately sometimes has more to do with the reader's natural ability to attune to the client's field than to the photograph or printout. And this will always be so, as technology follows the development and growth in human consciousness — not the other way round.

Therapists trained in Kinesiology and muscle-testing may also use such techniques successfully as a diagnostic method when determining which ray colours to treat in their patients.

Red Mist — Aura Phenomena

This is a common phenomenon in the astral body.

We call it the red mist, and sometimes the orange mist. In such situations, the red ray or orange ray rushes high up the aura, obscuring much of the other colours in the astral body, and leaving a thin spray of colour around the head. This occurs when we are under stress, often with our feelings out of control. Where the red mist predominates, we will experience degrees of anger, frustration and aggression, becoming very belligerent in extreme cases. When the orange predominates, which is less common, we feel weakened, even exhausted and unable to cope — this can often follow a surge of the red ray, the orange drawn up in its wake.

Such a phenomenon results from our lack of detachment and our tendency to be reactive to life, not in control, rather than creatively pro-active. We over-respond to challenges, allowing ourselves to become angry and exhausted. This is why we shake with anger — the power flows out of us quicker than it is flowing in.

Remedial Healing

For initial remedial action, we need to operate the rays in sequence.

1. The first part of the sequence is the application of the white ray and white essence, which will gradually disperse the red or orange mist. Some people hang onto their anger for longer than others and need longer treatments than others.

2. Once a calming has taken place, which it will do after such an application of light, we need to explore more dynamic long-term healing, in order to remove the tendency so that it does not happen again. The first application for this would be the red essence and ray, followed by orange. The length of time for each ray application will vary, but with careful observation and, if working with a therapist, some discussion, you will sense the changes in yourself and move on to apply the next colour.

3. Practice transmutation (page 120).

A female client of mine, a doctor, found that a particular individual always irritated her and angered her, giving her a headache as the mist formed. The white ray essence quickly eased the situation, and subsequent use of the red ray cleared the response altogether.

Sequence Prescribing

Earlier in the chapter, I mentioned the case of Pete, and the considerable improvements that unfolded in the healing in his yellow ray. It was, in fact, part of a sequence. First of all, he was given the white essence, to deal with the generally very confusing turmoil he was experiencing, especially in his solar plexus and his emotional body — when the solar plexus is not functioning well, neither is the emotional or astral field in us.

The yellow ray was used subsequently, to help bring the clarity and calmness, followed by the orange essence. Pete's response was quite dramatic and it was prescribed using the aura method (13E), involving the client's own reaction and input. Upon taking the orange essence and working with the orange ray, he became much more grounded and physically alive. He had experienced some psycho-sexual problems and had found his relationship with his wife, at the physical level, unattractive and verging on the repulsive.

The orange essence changed that significantly and he felt more 'in his body', and connected to the physical life more easily than he had done for many years. His sensuality had returned, and his wife was very pleased also. This gifted, sensitive man had begun to release fears and anxieties that had, for many years, damaged his physical relationship. He then went on to work with the red ray and essence to continue the healing process.

How Long to Heal?

Sequence healing of the emotions with the rays, and indeed at all levels, is an ongoing process. At all levels, but primarily the emotional and energetic, we have to initiate and then sustain our healing process. Times are changing rapidly and so are we.

We were seduced by the magic-bullet approach of allopathic medicine, but we discover that, as we broaden our view and experience of different therapeutics, we return to the notion of our healing as a journey from disease to ease, as a process in which we peel off the layers that obscure our highest, spiritual light and take us away from the ease which is natural for us.

As with all true healing, our early responses to our treatments are often the most dramatic as initial clearings take place. As the process develops, so our healing activity becomes more subtle, finer, and requires a deepening awareness and sensitive observation.

So, if you are working with a therapist, or alone, keep a journal in which you can record your progress; observe your feelings and the changes that occur. It is amazing how quickly, as healing occurs in us, we forget just how ill we were and, most importantly, how far we have travelled as we improve and become stronger and clearer.

When working with your light and your astral rays, you can move on to work with another ray at any time, as you will very likely return to the original colour later on, to make finer, more penetrating improvements to your emotional self.

Generally, you should work with a ray until improvements in your feelings and behaviour are evident, but you can cross-check by using the methods explored already. Use your intuition and you will be right. You cannot over-heal yourself, and every part of your emotional nature will require healing at some time.

Ray of Incarnation

In working on his healing, Pete, as is the case with many individuals, has one ray to which, I am sure, he may often return to more than he will return to some of the others in his aura. It is the orange ray.

Another individual, who is working with her therapist using the rays and the Flower Chromatic Essences, finds that the yellow ray is consistently most significant, and she frequently returns to it to sustain and continue the improvements she has made, whilst working with the other rays and essences intermittently.

This is because we have a Ray of Incarnation, a colour (sometimes two) which is the background light for our life upon the earth — this life.

It has a relationship to what classical homoeopaths refer to as the constitutional remedy. It would tend to be the ray or rays that seem to be the ones through which we express the greater part of our emotional energy and nature — the ray whose colour is pivotal in our life. We don't necessarily have any more of it visible in the aura than any other colour — it is simply more important.

It is possible to determine which ray this is by any one of the methods we have used already in selecting rays to work upon — in this instance, we simply ask for the Ray of Incarnation.

However, it is perhaps best to allow the ray to emerge naturally, in the course of normal prescribing and healing. You will soon discover what yours is as you return to it time and again as your emotions clear and stabilise.

Colourwise

As I have said before, my experience suggests that working with the rays and their colours is by far the best way of clearing, strengthening and healing the astral and emotional body. It is, after all, a body revealed to us through bright, coloured light, and so it is only sensible to see such direct working upon the rays as most useful.

In the next chapter, we will link with our mental body and selves, and consider how we can work towards mental freedom and ease. But our emotions literally 'colour our thoughts', and so it is through those colours that so much therapeutic change is possible in us. It is also important for us to connect with colour, enjoying and developing our relationship with the reflected light of our world. Such light can tell us so much of ourselves and our reality.

We should all be creative with colour, taking space to draw, paint or otherwise use colour, in order that we may express ourselves and explore our creative responses. Such activity is potentially very healing and helps us to connect with the light in the world around us in a fresh and uninhibited fashion.

Visit galleries and art exhibitions as often as you can. I myself always avail of the opportunity to visit the school my youngest son still attends, to view the vibrant creativity of the pupils as they reach into the world and record their reactions to its diversity and the message in its coloured palette.

Enjoy playing with colour. A garden gives us the most wonderful opportunity to be creative in such a way — or a patio or balcony.

Exercise 14 — Chakra Colouring

1. On a piece of paper, make a circle — I suggest something around the size of a small plate.
2. Find your centre, and in the stillness, think briefly of each of your major chakras or centres and how they are linked throughout your energy/etheric body, and also your astral body, to a beautiful web of light and myriad smaller, rotating centres, resting like wheels upon the surface of your astral body.
3. Choose one chakra, or centre, to focus upon. Let your feelings guide you as to which one you select.
4. As you focus upon this chakra, inside your head, allow your imagination to connect you to the swirls and pulses of coloured light within it. A veritable kaleidoscope will unfold for you.
5. After a while, return to normal consciousness, slowly grounding yourself through your feet, and slowly opening your eyes.
6. Using any colouring and drawing materials you have, and wish to use, celebrate the chakra and its light. It is not a question of copying what you saw or felt, but rather celebrating it, freely and happily. Take your time and enjoy it, using your circle as the space in which you work.

You will know when you have finished. And the act of drawing the centre itself is very healing. But you can use the drawing as a mandala or 'divine design', as a focus for some meditations.

Equally, explore the centre, asking questions of its message to you, especially in relation to your healing journey and your emotional field and body. In particular, it will help you to understand which rays in you need healing most at this time. You will have chosen this chakra because it is important for you, and it may be good to return to this centre several times

— alongside your therapist if you are working with one — repeating the exercise and noting the changes that take place. Trust your feelings and your choices, and make notes in your journal of any information it may give to you.

Later, you can move on and work with another of the major centres, until you have explored them all and the astral light they radiate and absorb. It will be a wonderful, creative journey, which you may develop into a deep dialogue. Observe the changes that take place in your feelings as you continue on your way, and heal the emotional energy in your centres of light.

On my workshops, we frequently engage in such an activity — it is always popular and useful, and it is always healing for those who participate.

A Table of Correspondences

As stated earlier, diagnosis in the use of the rays in emotional healing is most effectively made by the methods I have introduced in this chapter. We have to learn to think and prescribe in terms of colour values and interpretation. This table of general correspondences is not absolute, as no such table can be. It is, however, useful as a general check, perhaps, once we have made our diagnosis. Where such intuitive diagnosis may seem at odds with how the reader interprets this table, stay with the intuition — the links here may make more sense later on, once a healing sequence has been followed through for a while.

NB: The intuition is a significant feature of all rays, but especially those indicated by an ★ in the table on the page opposite.

Ray	Mental and Emotional Issues	Destiny Issues
Silver	Quest for perfection and management of female (moon) & male nature.	*Intuition* Yin/Yang — Pos/Neg. Divine love & soul connection. Links with angels.
White	Uninspired. Cut off from 'dreams' and hopes. No sense of connection. Spiritual emptiness. Shock, panic.	Spirituality. Inspiration & Connection.
Violet/ Purple	Lack of imagination. No 'vision'. Unwillingness to 'see' matters. No confidence. Lack of initiative. Terrifying or confusing dreams. Extreme sensitivity. No awareness of others.	Perception. Vision & Action *Intuition*
Blues	Lack of creativity. Expressionless. Talking too much or too little. Poor listener. No ideals or ideas. Difficulties with balance between inner and outer communication.	Vocation. Creative Self-Expression.
Turquoise	Dishonesty. Fear of truth. Closed mind. Unwillingness to change.	Truth and Honesty.
Peach	Relationships (general). Need for peace and inner calm. Lacking in diplomacy and tact. Brusque and uncharitable towards others.	Peacefulness. Acceptance. Conciliation.
Rose	Coldness. Cannot give or receive affection. Feeling unloved. Close relationships break down easily or are difficult to form.	Love and affection.
Green	Lack of trust. 'Poverty'. Lack of balance. Meanness, no generosity. Unwillingness to change. Tendency to feel victimised. Without compassion.	Love and wisdom. Understanding. *Intuition* Growth and change.
Yellow	Fear. Anxiety. Hastiness. Clarity of mind. Feelings of worthlessness. Selfishness. Intellectual extremes and ruthlessness. Mental arrogance. Ambition.	Need. Higher desire.
Orange	Weakness. Powerlessness. No vitality. Sexual difficulties and fertility problems. Difficulties with sensuality and physical aspect of relationships.	Power.
Red	Difficulties with will and will to live. Vagueness. Lack of direction. Sexual difficulties. Impotence. Anger. Extreme sensuality. Tendency to change course too easily.	Purpose.

CHAPTER 5

MIND AND MENTAL HEALING

As a man thinketh in his heart, so is he.

Proverbs 23.7

Mind over Matter

I had known Jo for many years. Our children had attended the same schools, and she had helped me on many occasions in some of my musical endeavours, as she was a fine and highly gifted musician. She had consulted me occasionally for a little guidance and sometimes for healing. However, a visit to her GP had revealed a lump in her right breast, and the subsequent investigation in hospital diagnosed breast cancer. Jo came to see me to discuss the situation, to have healing, and to explore the options before her. Surgery, radiotherapy, and possible chemotherapy, had been advised urgently, as the cancer was viewed as being quite aggressive.

'I don't want to go down that route,' she told me. 'It is so wrapped in fear and negativity, and I already feel the power and decision being taken away from me. I want to use my mind, and find an alternative approach.'

Jo was a very determined soul, and she wasn't willing to concede to anything with which she didn't agree. She had been like that as long as I had known her. She wasn't aggressive or belligerent, but she was not the kind of individual simply to accept that there is only one route, one way of approaching anything, including her own health and healing.

She decided to reject the orthodox approach. Now, I am always very cautious when an individual with such a view comes to me for help. Not that it is not a viable approach, because it is and our thoughts ultimately have a remarkable effect upon our bodies and reality. But I do understand the importance of our belief system and, however much we may wish to accept and avail ourselves of the mental, spiritual, holistic ways of healing, it is equally vital to understand that our conditioning and cultural patterns also develop in us a very deep-seated belief in conventional, orthodox medicine. In the mental body, these entrenched thought forms are very clear to see, usually being well established by the time we reach adolescence, and often earlier. As the Jesuits would say, 'Give me the child at birth, and by seven I will give you the man.' Such thoughts are, of course, removable — it is our nature to release old, limiting thoughts and mental patterns, and seek new, more expansive ones — but that can take time for us to achieve, and patience is, perhaps, the greatest quality we have to learn and demonstrate. Hence my advice to most souls is to use the best of all worlds, and consider a multi-disciplinary approach to their healing needs. God can guide the surgeon's hand as much as the healer's, and we should always remember that.

Equally, I understood how Jo felt. And I respected her right to seek and exercise control over her own destiny — and that includes her physical well-being as she saw it.

So, she took the situation full on, as they say, using her mind to reorganise her thinking, diluting and removing redundant thought patterns and replacing them with new ones. Her healing package included visits to a homoeopath, to use the vibration of his remedies upon her energy body, and also healing and mental work with me. She used her mind to be creative with the light in her imagination, energising images which emerged through her pineal gland, in the magnetic field around the head, created as we saw in Chapter 3. Jo was attracting to herself powerful thought forms, energising them, and changing the nature of her thinking and, ultimately, her reality.

The lump gradually disappeared and, years later, it shows no signs of returning. Jo had harnessed her thinking and changed her experience, and whilst some may fail in the attempt, what one person does, others can, and eventually will do.

Thought Streams

Our mental body is another glorious wonder to behold. It exists in two forms. The lower mental body overlays the astral/emotional, energy/etheric, and physical bodies, and is the level in us through which our thoughts emerge and are concrete and identifiable. We never stop thinking, and we exist because we are an aspect of the thoughts of our creator or source. Yogananda said that the universe is one big thought, containing many lesser, smaller ones, including ourselves.

Many aspiring meditators express the desire to 'blank the mind'. Not only is that impossible, but it is also undesirable, and what they are really seeking is to attain, through meditation, access to that other, higher mental self. At this level, we interact directly with the soul, and with the universe, still thinking or having individualised thoughts, but these thoughts are abstract and, hence, non-figurative in the way that our pictures and visions are in our lower, concrete minds. From our soul, the higher mental self passes to our personality and lower mind pure thoughts and ideas, so that our lower mind may recognise them.

We are bombarded with ever-increasing thought streams and groups of thought forms filled with energy by those around us. As we think, so we attract, and that is why, so often, thoughts seem to spread through groups, crowds, and even entire nations, when we become receptive to them by adopting similar attitudes and ideas within our own mental field. We become a mental magnet and, sometimes, a mental sponge.

We accumulate such thoughts both in this lifetime and in others, both the earthly ones and other lives. Some thoughts are generational and are handed on to us through our parents. Other thought patterns stay with us from other lives, as we have not processed them and freed ourselves from their influence (see Figure 5.1).

Figure 5.1: Thought streams flowing into aura

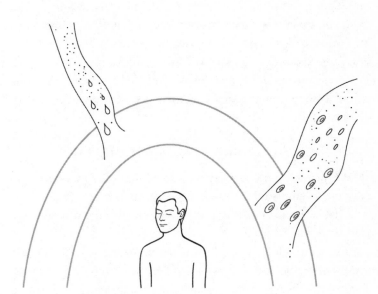

When we begin meditation, we are trying initially to concentrate and control our thoughts, choosing what to think. Usually, the thought streams continue, reminding us of all the things we should and could be doing instead of meditating! This is indicative of the great waves and streams of ever-increasing ideas we encounter day by day. We will deal with meditation in more detail later.

As the earth quickens and changes, and we approach a new and emerging consciousness, so the volume of information we are expected to process, particularly at the lower level, grows, and the thought streams thicken, confusing us, making us feel as if we will never be able to cope, never having enough time and space to deal with everything. This isn't really the case, but it feels like it.

Our minds are expanding and we can process far more thoughts and ideas — it is simply that we are receiving a bottom-heavy load. Instead of accessing from our souls and higher minds the higher, dynamic, most appropriate thoughts, we are awash with the trivia of our information age, much of which seeks to persuade, control and manipulate us, particularly through the media — radio, TV, press, advertising, and so on.

So, it is for us to be alert, awake and vigilant, aware and conscious of our thoughts and our mental bodies, through which they travel.

New Thought, Magic, Religion

The Aquarian, New Age, as it is sometimes called, is offering to us a great opportunity if we can see through much of the dross that has accumulated around it, and work with the true message and potential it heralds.

Even our old religions are being re-evangelised as the last throes of the Sixth Esoteric Ray of Devotion slides out of focus. Fundamentalism and fanaticism raise their heads, and distorted magical practices abound — casting out demons, faith (as opposed to spiritual) healing, talking in tongues (some valid, but much gibberish), and hypnotic mind control by repetitious chanting. All non-thinking devotees of whatever religion become convinced that theirs is the only way, and that any good person will surrender to it, forsaking all others (and all other thoughts!). It is the worst form of mental disease, and awakening from it can cause disillusionment and pain, along with a sense of void and emptiness.

Good mental activity and controlled, conscious thinking provide the pathway to the true magic of being. With an open, creative mind, we can achieve and be anything we can imagine.

Visualisation, as it is now called, is the practice of the magician — imaging in our minds the things we wish to see in our lives, prior to bringing them into manifestation in the material world. These days, even sports psychologists use this mental magic, and we are all encouraged to visualise things as they should be, to see ourselves scoring goals and winning races.

The word 'magic' is a derivative of the Persian word, *magus*, which means 'wise one', or 'wise man', one who has mastery over himself and hence mastery over his world. Unfortunately, sorcery and black magic have also appeared, based largely on self-ishness and fear. True magic is the wise and loving use of the self for the common good, as per the Christian gospels in the west, for Jesus taught magic — 'if anyone says this to a mountain, *get up and move yourself into the sea*, with no hesitation in his heart, but believing that what he says will happen, it will be done for him. I tell you therefore, everything you ask and pray for, believe that you have it already, and it will be yours.' (Mark 11:23)

Magic is wisdom and creativity flowing powerfully through a loving heart — the true path to mental ease and complete health. We must always think through our hearts.

In this chapter, we will explore some of the key issues I see in my work as central to a clear mind and healthy, creative mental processes. There are many approaches and avenues the reader may venture down, but these issues are important and significant, whatever path you may choose.

Honesty and Openness

Some years ago, I was consulted by Theo, a therapist from Northern Germany. He was generally quite well, wishing mainly to have a little guidance in his session, and comments upon his work with his clients. The only complaint he had was of a slightly irritating pressure at the top of his chest, which led to his continually seeking to clear his throat, as if there was something lodging there. Examination by a physician had revealed nothing wrong physically — no infection or inflammation or any other discernible problem. None the less, Theo found this very irritating, as did his wife.

I had noticed this before, in others — presenting the same symptom picture and also absence of any pathology or infection. In each case, the chakra above the heart centre, which I have termed the meta-heart, has been in a state of powerful activity, rather like a cog in a machine that is being speeded up, so that the machine can work more quickly, more dynamically. And I have observed it many times, though not exclusively, in either a therapist or someone whose work has a strong social and, perhaps, communication dimension to it.

It became clear to me that this centre has a very special role in Theo's situation and, in most people, it is one of the emerging or 'new' chakras — new in the sense that it is just now coming into a fuller expression in mankind.

The main connection of the meta-heart is with the forces of honesty and openness, which in our age is truly significant. Its awakening heralds a real, empowering, yet daunting, challenge for us all, for it is telling us that we have to be straight in our dealings — clear and open. Fading are the times in which we can hide behind lies and falsehoods, secrecy and deceit, and we have to move forward into the light of the truth in us. Life is asking us to be who we truly are and not to seek to be false, wearing a mask to hide behind, concealing our true nature.

In fact, we are being asked to be God-like — loving, creative, wise and generous. It is interesting how we seek to hang onto secrecy, even when old patterns are breaking down, and those structures designed to obscure the truth are crumbling with them. As nations, we still have spies, secret services who are responsible for 'intelligence' — discovering what is really happening in other places.

Our politicians give us spin — manipulate the media to control how we perceive what is happening in public affairs whatever the truth may be. But, increasingly, it is to no avail, as this centre unfolds in us the capacity to discriminate between the truth, the half-truths and the lies.

The secret banking, off-shore accounts, the hidden lives of our public figures who preach one thing and do another — these are all collapsing now, and dishonest practices will become more and more difficult to sustain. I have many good friends in the principality of Liechtenstein, nestling between Switzerland and Austria — a tiny country of some 30,000 people. On my first visit, I was aware of the reputation of Liechtenstein as an offshore centre, renowned for secret bank accounts. I remember commenting at the time that 1999 would be the beginning of the end for such secrecy. (This first visit was in 1995.)

During 1999, a former German Chancellor, Helmut Kohl, was the subject of public revelations concerning secret political financial dealings in which he had been involved via Liechtenstein. The subsequent turmoil in that country, and also offshore centres, has been considerable as the unacceptability of secrecy increases.

Liechtenstein is a beautiful place and has many other success-ful and highly creative industries, but the offshore business, or at least its more undesirable aspects, is now breaking up as will all such businesses around the globe. This is inevitable as the meta-heart opens in us and precipitates a more honest world. Can you imagine a world where lies and deceit become impossible to conceal? This is what the meta-heart is opening for us as we journey towards the new consciousness.

Clarity of Perception

My friend Theo is not dishonest especially — he is a good man and has a very sound approach to life. His difficulties with this centre were, in part, developmental, for, as we grow, we experience periods of adjustment which are often a little uncomfortable, and sometimes, as Theo had, we have physical tensions, of a temporary nature, located close to the relevant chakra. To be an even better therapist, Theo would need even more clarity as to why his clients are experiencing the problems they are; the opening of the meta-heart will give him access to deep insights and the truth behind the disease and difficulties his clients present. It will also mean that he — as all of us — will have to be ever more honest with himself and in his dealings with others.

We cannot hide any longer.

Exercise 15 — Opening to the Meta Heart and Clarity

1. Sit quietly where you will not be disturbed, and find the centre, radiating your beautiful light.
2. Focus your attention back upon your meta-heart centre, at the top of your chest. In the mental body, this centre is like a beautiful, perfectly balanced flower, with petals of light around its circumference.
3. Breathe deeply through this centre, allowing three slow breaths to enter it from the front, flow through, and pass out the back of the centre and its vortex as you exhale. As you do this, the light of the meta-heart becomes brighter, clearer and indescribably beautiful.
4. Think of the life around you: the people with whom you share the world — family, friends, colleagues and others. Work from this centre outwards as you think of them one at a time. With each one, bless them and thank them for being in your life.
5. Imagine a beautiful link between you and everyone, connecting to each of the chakras or centres in your mental body, connecting mind to mind perfectly.

6. Focus upon the meta-heart and how the light of this centre determines that, from now on, your relationships with everyone will be based upon honesty and clarity — a new liberating openness that will set everyone free. We are dishonest with each other only because we have forgotten how splendid and glorious we really are.
7. Focus upon your meta-heart again. You will feel the difference. Relationships will change, and life will offer to you so much more wisdom and opportunity.
8. Briefly find your centre again, before grounding yourself through your feet, and then returning slowly to normal consciousness.

You have begun to open a very special and remarkable door. You will begin to see yourself and others with renewed clarity and ease. And life will never be able to deceive you if you exercise your meta-heart and connect with its forces.

One friend had great problems with her sister-in-law who she felt was rather disingenuous, never really honest with her. As a consequence, a substantial mental barrier had grown between them, and my friend was always tense, negative and fearful when her sister-in-law was due to visit.

She worked with the forces of her meta-heart, and gradually her thinking about her sister-in-law changed and eased. She really began to see her in a different light, and her sister-in-law also appeared more open, frank, and conciliatory in their conversations. The tensions between them dissipated and they both became much more comfortable and trusting in each other's company.

Now

As we take another view of the meta-heart and the heart chakra or centre, its next-door neighbour in the mental body, to be truly healed, we have to live totally in the moment and release the past with its thoughts and memories into the time in which it exists, allowing the future to come as it may. We find this very difficult.

Some of us are great worriers. We worry about what we could have done in the past to make things different — 'if only I had ...' — never satisfied in the moment, always looking for what we should have changed. We also fear the future, anxious about what horrors or disappointments life may have in store for us — 'But what if ....'

Yet the past is gone; we can do nothing about it now. And whatever we are in life, the future is malleable, changeable according to our thoughts and attitudes. To live in the moment as fully as possible is the perfect attitude and mind-set. In so doing, we liberate ourselves, recovering the power which opens us to a creative, enhanced future experience.

The dynamics of this are clear and, to be healed in our minds, we must embrace them and work with them.

The Dynamics of Now

1. We need to release the past and allow energy into the present through forgiveness — forgiveness of ourselves and forgiveness of others.
2. We then learn to accept the moment — knowing that wherever we are, whatever we are, is right for us at that moment, and from there we can grow, create, change and improve.
3. We then need to anticipate the future in love and trust and away from fear — true creativity.

When our thoughts dwell in the past, we direct back through our consciousness, into the past, some of the energy we absorb through our etheric energy bodies to use in this moment. We all know people who seem to live in the past and don't wish to leave it for one reason or another. We cannot function fully if we live in such a way.

So we have to connect with the forces in our hearts and meta-hearts, releasing that which has gone, and especially those things we see as shortcomings in ourselves or others. Such thinking sets us free, allowing us to bring our power back into the present day and experience the healing that will bring to us.

Exercise 16 — Bringing the Thoughts and Energy from the Past to the Present

1. Relax and breathe deeply, finding your centre.
2. Focus upon your heart chakra vortex, in the centre of your chest. It is a beautiful vortex of clear light. Just above it is the meta-heart, equally clear, bright and open.
3. Radiating from the space between these two vortices, are strands of mental energy, linking you with your past — everyone you have been, everything you have done. We are blessed with memory and remember everything.
4. Also, there are some other strands of energy, connecting you with your anticipated future — the options that lie ahead of you.
5. Linking with your incoming breath, imagine any of the energy you have been directing to the past flowing back towards you now, into the space between your heart and meta-heart, giving you increased power to live in the moment. Think the word 'Now' as this happens.
6. After a few moments, imagine the same pattern as you link with the energy strands you are pushing into the unknown future. Breathe deeply and allow the energy to flow back to you, again thinking the word 'Now' as the pulses of energy come to you.

7. Your energy levels will rise as you do this — with practice, you will feel and sense the change. Finally, focusing in the heart-centre vortex, make the affirmation, 'I live now, totally, in this moment', three times.
8. Gradually draw your attention back, connecting with the earth through your feet, before opening your eyes slowly and returning to everyday consciousness.

Practised regularly, such an exercise frees your mind, giving you more mental energy for whatever task you encounter, and gradually diluting the hold the past may have on you and any fear you may have of the future.

As one woman said to me, 'I didn't realise the present could be so wonderful.'

Forgiveness

Whilst I have dealt with forgiveness a little in earlier writings, particularly in *Being Loving is Being Healthy* (LN Fowler 1987), this is a most important activity for the healing of the self. It is an aspect of moving from Fear into Love, from solar plexus and emotional clouding, to heart compassion, mental equilibrium, wisdom and love.

Forgiveness is fundamental to all healing and is often misunderstood. Forgiveness is necessary for both the forgiver and the forgiven. People who hold resentments gradually reduce their energy flow — both physical and mental — for a creative, active life, and lay themselves open to all manner of low-energy disease, such as some forms of cancer, diabetes and digestive problems, poor eyesight, fatigue, nervous exhaustion, anxiety, and a whole range of immune deficiency conditions. How can our bodies keep us healthy today, when we are still angry about yesterday?

Sexual promiscuity and the hidden guilt we feel as a consequence, whatever we might try to do to justify it in our own minds, also plays a part here, and we cord or link our energy into an emotional sea of connections, with our thoughts and energy straying backwards. Sometimes we feel angry with those we have left behind, or with ourselves for being so shallow and selfish in our pursuit of short-term pleasure and gratification.

Aids was a disease waiting to happen, and we cannot cure it simply through drugs, for even if we appear to succeed, something else will replace it. We have to learn to be clear in our thinking and live in the moment with our relationships, but equally honour the needs of our souls and those of others, as well as the needs of our physical and lower emotional selves and bodies.

We will consider sexual energy and the mental chakras later, but for now — whatever has gone before, it is time to leave it behind.

Forgiveness may not immediately change our feelings towards someone who has hurt us and for whom we feel resentment, anger or hatred. What forgiveness does is enable us to take action to get on with our lives, to be more creative and to start the process of dilution of our past connections. The attitudes and subsequent feelings usually change gradually. But in forgiveness we are taking control again, bringing more and more of our power into the moment and, equally, setting others free to get on with their own lives.

We suspend judgment and begin to learn and grow from our experience, however painful it may at first seem. We stop visiting old sites in our life's landscape, ceasing to behave like an unimaginative tourist who is afraid to go forward to visit new locations and cross new horizons.

Accept the experience, however painful. You cannot change it — it is gone. Know from now on that things can and will improve if you think creatively about yourself and your life, truly moving on.

Another way to look at forgiveness is to understand that you harm yourself unless you do forgive. If you see yourself as a victim, you are making yourself a victim all over again. And you cannot punish the one you view as perpetrator. You may be angry with them, but any punishment you inflict on them, any bad thoughts you have or destructive actions you take will come hurtling back to you sevenfold in the karmic process of cause and effect.

There are many forgiving exercises that can free the mind and clear the mental body. Here is one I learned many years ago, which I still use occasionally on workshops — it is very powerful and yet very gentle. On a healing course I ran many years ago, after we tried this exercise, one dear lady said, much to the amusement of the other students, 'Boy, I needed that!'

Exercise 17 (A) — Forgiveness, Flying Along

1. Find your centre.
2. Bring your thoughts to your heart, seeing it or sensing it as a beautiful centre of marvellous coloured light.
3. Slowly bring your focus upwards through your heart, through your meta-heart, into your head, until you reach the space between your brow centre and the crown chakra — the link between the pituitary and pineal glands, where the pictures form inside your imagination.
4. Imagine a clear day in the open air — blue skies, a very slight, warm breeze, and beautiful countryside. Close by is a small, magical aircraft waiting for you to fly in. Remember it is a magic plane, rather like the open, propeller-driven bi-planes of years gone by — the Stearman training planes that still grace an airfield near here on flying days.
5. Board your plane, put on your goggles and rev up the engine. You are the pilot and you are in control.

6. Taxi across the airstrip before taking off and flying high in the air. You are perfectly safe — you have a magic plane that knows exactly what to do and it will carry you safely anywhere.

7. As you fly high, enjoy the view and the breeze on your face. Beneath you are fields and woodlands, and in the distance you can see a figure — someone walking and waving in the air at you. This figure is the embodiment of anyone you still focus upon negatively, perhaps whom you resent or see as someone you need to forgive. Wave back at them and circle overhead for a while.

8. In the seat next to you, you have a gift for them. It is a delicious trifle, with custard, jelly and all sorts of delicious things in it. And you know how much they like that. You tip the trifle out from the plane and it falls through the air towards them, splattering all over them. They lick their lips and love it — it is a shower of delight for them, and a funny gift from you. See them wave to you with a smile as they walk off. You have made quite an impact.

9. Circle your plane for a while and let it bring you gently downwards, landing safely on the field from which you had embarked. They are fine and so are you. Later on, you can let them fly the magic aeroplane whilst you receive some special trifle, chocolate pudding or whatever you wish from them. It will not harm you or them, but it will free the tension between you and, I hope, give you a smile.

10. When you have finished your flight(s), visit the changing room on the corner of the airfield and enjoy a nice warm shower, washing away the connection (and any trifle that is left.)

11. Place your thought in your heart for a while, before returning to everyday consciousness, connecting with the earth and slowly opening your eyes. You may find that having a real shower after this exercise is also useful.

Exercise 17 (B) — Forgiveness, Garden of Light
As an alternative, you might find this exercise valuable.

1. Visit your Garden of Light, as in Exercise 12 in Chapter 4.
2. Find your quiet corner and sit there for a moment, enjoying the stillness and love with which it nurtures you.
3. Next to you is a small picture book. Pick it up and open it. Inside is a photograph of those you love and have loved in this life. Thank them for that love and sprinkle a few flower petals on their pictures.
4. Further on in the book are pictures of those you need to forgive. As you view them, you may feel some sensation in your solar plexus. If you do, that is natural, as your thoughts are still clouded with negative emotional energy held there. Bring that feeling upwards into your heart centre — as you do, it will begin to melt away and clear your thoughts, setting you free. Sprinkle a few beautiful flower petals upon their picture. In your heart, say the words, 'I forgive you. I move on now.'
5. Take a deep breath, look around your garden, and then return through the entrance.
6. Find your centre again, before slowly returning to normal consciousness.
   You can repeat this exercise if you wish to forgive and release yourself from guilt and what you perceive to be old patterns and redundant experiences. There will be a picture of you in your book if you need one.

When you have worked at this healing, you will become more at ease. You will certainly have more mental energy. Do it as often as you feel you need to, and each time you have finished it, seek out an opportunity to do something generous and kind for someone, anyone at all. It need not be a huge or lavish gesture, just something simple, unrequested and unexpected. That will affirm your experience and continue to balance the relationship between your solar plexus and your heart centre as you develop a more forgiving mind.

The Karmic Roll or Cycle

Much has been written about the law of karma, the Sanskrit term for cause and effect, reaping and sowing, and I have no wish to duplicate it here. However, it may be useful to explain it a little more from the point of view of clarity, and how we can heal ourselves, lifting our consciousness into the highest part of our mental nature.

We live in a sequence of experiences which we call time — it is largely a linear journey which allows us to explore space and that which we perceive within it.

Our souls, or higher selves, lead us through this process, in this world and in others, both in a sequence of lives here upon the earth and in other space–time dimensions. Between the human life-times we experience in this physical plane, and also in what we term sleep, we are active in other lives, other realities, and, from the point of view of our soul or higher-self, life is a complex series of continuums, all connected as part of a whole eternal experience.

Lives we have led in the past, still exist in their own time-frame, and the future options wait for us like a series of costumes for us to wear and to energise with our attention.

As we think, we set in motion a process that ultimately, through the thoughts our minds project, becomes surrounded with emotional and etheric/energetic substance, materialising in our physical world as our experience. And we are inclined to repeat experiences until we learn from them, let go of them and move on to new creative opportunity.

What is important for us to realise is that all the experience we now have is the consequence of our thoughts and actions, from earlier lives, but predominantly from this one.

As we become more aware and begin to understand our experiences, so we release them and become lighter. Our mental aura becomes brighter, the rays within it more silvery or metallic in their colours, radiating clear, constructive thoughts and ideas downwards through to our personality.

As we learn and understand, so the centre of our consciousness shifts 'upwards', for the karmic roll has awakened us, and, instead of being victims tossed around, powerless in the tides of life and the experiences therein, we become creative, begin to have an increasingly elevated and enlightened view of life, and realise that, far from being powerless, we are totally powerful. We become aware that we are causes, not effects.

In such awakening, the old, limiting thought processes are left behind and we connect with those in our higher mind, closer to our souls. We then work in tune with the universe and our own spiritual nature, seeking to fulfil our destiny and, most important, being happy and willing to help and allow everyone else to do the same.

Notions of competition, limitation and shortage, and the fear, greed and selfishness accompanying them, evaporate as we realise that we live in a potentially unlimited reality and that we can be creative within that for the good of all. We become truly enlightened, enabling the light of the higher mind and soul to work through our concrete mind and to find the peace and true love such unfolding brings. That is what we call a *State of Grace* — nothing else matters apart from celebrating Love, Wisdom and the Joy of Being.

That is thinking through the heart for the collective good, in a world of infinite possibilities, rather than through the solar plexus, for the self, in a world of finite thinking and selfishness. In these changing times, such things are asked of us, as old 'securities' — job for life, pension, investments, status and so on — fall away and we are called to be open, flexible and heart-centred, living in the moment, connected to our soul, expansive and trusting in our thinking.

Figure 5.2: The Karmic roll or cycle

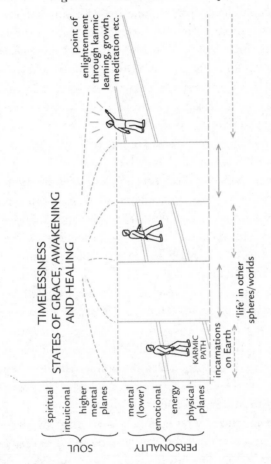

Monica's Story

Whilst writing this section, I received a fax from a client in Europe. Monica is a psychotherapist who trained and studied with a very eminent teacher and practitioner in the field. A favourite student of his, she became close both to the professor and to his family — she said, 'He and his wife often called me their daughter.' And he had grown to mean a lot to her. 'He became a very close person in my life — friend, father-figure, trainer, teacher, mentor etc. I am very thankful and deeply connected with him, and love him.'

However, Monica's teacher is very ill and has a form of cancer with which he is gradually deteriorating, and he appears to be dying. He cannot really teach and work any more and announced that he wanted her to work in a practice he had set up with a relative of his, with the aim of continuing the work he had begun and developed over the years. Monica, on the other hand, feels that the time has come 'to stand on my own two feet, grow up'. She feels no special connection with her teacher's relative, but still honours her teacher and respects him and what he did for her.

Meanwhile, she has been offered work in another practice, where she worked as a student. She likes both the established partners of this practice, feels very pleased with the offer, and wishes to take it up. It is a very established clinic of some twenty years' standing.

Monica's teacher has reacted badly and has issued an ultimatum to her. She said, 'He feels I want to leave him, and, therefore, if I go, he will have to cut off all the personal and professional relationships.' He told her that she had hurt him and let him down. He also ridiculed the other practice — a practice he founded and sold to the present owners — and said that it was competition for him and his relative.

For a man who is suffering from a low-energy disease — as all cancer is — this is poor thinking to espouse. It is very centred in his solar plexus and lower mental self, covered in negative emotions which he uses to try to control Monica and manipulate her. Whatever he may or may not feel, his limited thinking is damaging him further, as well as causing Monica much pain. 'I am now desperate,' she wrote.

This is a classic heart versus solar plexus imbalance and is central to so many of our relationships. Instead of thinking generously and being happy for Monica's growth and opportunity, her teacher returns to self and fear, and loses connection with his higher knowledge and values. There is no real competition in the universe, only that which our mind perceives. With such thinking, Monica's tutor is lowering, further still, the forces, energy patterns and vitality in his mental, emotional and physical bodies.

I think that Monica will follow her higher vision and look again to her heart as it seeks to lead her to pastures new and fresh experiences.

Mental Chakra Connections

At this time, the iridescent light of the mental body is difficult to describe and, for many, to imagine, so we will work with the mental chakras. There are some important chakra vortex connections which are vital in our mental healing, and thus our healing generally. These can best be delineated as follows:

Predominantly Electrical in Nature

Chakra/Centre vortex	Universal Force	Main Level of Expression	Some Organs that Correspond to the Chakra
Head/Crown	Spiritual Will	Spiritual/Soul Plane	Brain, Eyes, Pineal Gland
Brow/Eyes/Nose	Soul Force	Soul/ Higher Mental Plane	Brain, Eyes, Nose, Nerves
Mouth/Throat/Chin★	Creative Intelligence	Mental Plane	Breathing, Hearing
Meta Heart/Heart	Group awareness and life force. Love and wisdom	Higher Mental Plane	Heart, Circulation, Blood and Vegus Nerve

Predominantly Magnetic

Chakra/Centre vortex	Universal Force	Main Level of Expression	Some Organs that Correspond to the Chakra
Solar Plexus★	Emotion, Desire	Astral/Emotional Plane	Stomach, Liver, Gall Bladder, Sympathetic Nervous System
Abdomen★	Energy and Vital Force	Etheric energetic plane	Generative Organs
Root★/*Base*	Personal Will	Physical plane Earthly world	Spinal Structure, Kidneys and Adrenals

★ Centres primarily connected to the personality.

Again, it is right to point out that any correspondences beyond three dimensions are not absolute — they cannot be. But these may be useful as we consider the chakra links in the mental body and the transforming thought processes that go with them, as we seek to clear the channels between our higher and lower mental and emotional bodies, becoming more healthy and at ease.

Abdomen and Throat Centre —
The Creative, Expressive Mind

One of the most powerful links that frequently creates problems in our mental body is the relationship between the abdominal and throat centres. So much of our thinking and creativity is governed by our sexuality, and whilst we should always joyfully celebrate our sexual interaction with those we love, our cultural ethos tends to encourage us to exploit it as a negotiating tool through life's myriad experiences. From the abdominal chakra (along with the solar plexus), we make powerful connections called cords, which are really subtle tubes or strands of thought, often laced with emotion; these cords express the nature of the relationship we have with others. Where there is a strong sexual and deeply personal link, the abdomen is involved.

So-called powerful people — by which we usually mean controlling, manipulative, and often aggressive individuals who are power-seeking — often have difficulties here, and many such souls have affairs and relationships outside their permanent partnerships. Sadly, the power they use often goes into overload and damages them, either physically with sexual disease, or ultimately with low-energy disease such as cancer.

And these people are often damaged emotionally, and eventually mentally, when they are 'found out'. Because of the strong link with the throat centre, they are often talkers, and certainly like to be heard, with many, many ideas and, perhaps, with a 'finger in many pies'.

Idealism and a sense of vocation have often been the underpinning to their lives, but sometimes it has become lost as ambition, and the love of status and control has taken over. Literally, they cannot keep the balance between the abdomen and the throat. The abdomen wins, and the throat is depleted, usually making them ill, maybe beginning with throat infections, and other disease with its source in the respiratory system and the glands of the neck or mouth. Glandular fever has its energetic and mental roots here.

Other problems in this centre relationship are revealed as poor mental energy and concentration, weak self-expression, poor communication skills and an unwillingness truly to hear what others are saying. The poor communication skills are frequently found in the extremes — both a chatterbox who never listens and seldom really answers a question, and the tongue-tied type, fearful to express themselves, afraid that what they have to say might not really be deemed important.

Most commonly in this dynamic relationship, we are using too much mental energy in the abdomen and insufficient in the throat. Where the throat is dominant, we see the other extreme: weak people, allowing themselves to be pushed around (they don't want to be), they may be 'all-talk but no-action' types. They'll be full of ideas, usually exaggerated, often tearful and their voice may become notably high pitched as they become excited or agitated. Asthma may manifest in such souls, and in any dynamic involving this relationship, there could be breathing difficulties, ear problems and a tendency to light-headedness. They need massage, sensual and physical activities like sculpture and gardening, and practical activities of all kinds.

One individual I knew with a great problem here was highly intelligent — they often are — and when she chose, could be very articulate. However, she always resorted to sensual ways of justifying herself, and was very promiscuous. She used her sexuality as a power tool. And she had no need of that — she could be bright and articulate, and, as is also common with such souls, vocation was something important to her, although she usually ignored those idealistic urgings until they burst out in almost violent explosions of frustration at the menial and tedious nature of her life, and the dreams and sense of 'wanting to help, do something with meaning' burning, but mostly suppressed, within her. These centres are a common problem amongst teachers, preachers and politicians, although by no means exclusively.

Another thinking trait often connected with an imbalance here is that tendency to place others upon a pedestal, to view others as so much more important than ourselves. I call it 'pedestalling'! It is akin to hero worship — needing people to look up to — and consequently we can compare ourselves with them in very inferior light.

Such people often tend to be disappointed and feel let down by life when the person on the pedestal falls off, failing to live up to the idealistic, devotional adulation. In such situations, there is often a battle, with sexual energy in the individual leading to extremes of sexual behaviour.

Exercise 18 (A) — Healing Action and Integration
To bring equilibrium into the dynamic exchange between these two centres,

1. Relax and find the centre.
2. Connect with the abdominal chakra/centre and its great vortex of light. Imagine it as being full of physical, creative energy, bathed in orange light.
3. Now connect with the throat centre. Again, see its vortex of light and imagine this centre to be full of creative, intelligent mental energy. Imagine this centre as blue.
4. Imagine three strands of orange light lifting up from your abdomen, weaving through your heart centre into your throat centre, and then three strands of blue light, moving down to your abdominal centre, also travelling through your heart. As this happens, be aware that a balance is being established in your creative energy, between your physical creativity and your mental levels. This blending is perfect.
5. With the throat chakra more open, so that you can express yourself clearly, with power and ease, think the following affirmation three times: 'I am perfectly creative. I express myself clearly, with power and ease.'
6. Breathe deeply for a few moments, contemplating the balanced link that has been established, and the healing it brings to you, before grounding yourself, and returning slowly to normal awareness.

Repeated often, this exercise will be most empowering and will help you to develop your creative intelligence, focusing your power exactly where it needs to be.

One young man, who initially worked with this approach, found that his ambition completely changed. Instead of wishing to influence and impress others, he began to develop a new sense of his own purpose, and how he could express that. He changed careers; his partnership became happier, more at ease; he found himself listening to others more, able to think more clearly about life and what mattered; but most of all, he became very gentle — a little like a gentle giant. His persistent sore throats also vanished.

Solar Plexus, Brow and Eye Centres
Image and Vision
As our society is encouraged to live in the solar plexus, it is hardly surprising that our perception and vision of ourselves and life are very limited.

As well as being a major processor of emotional energy in the astral self, and a measurer of space and dimension in the energy body, the solar plexus is the threshold that stands between human, personality-based thinking, with its tendency to limited, finite models of reality, and the expansive, idealistic visions and ideas that our heart and head will offer to us if we dare to slip out of the solar plexus, stop being afraid, and work towards the greatest higher desires in us. This is the true role of the solar plexus in the mental body — through our own need and the desire in us to fulfil that need creatively and expansively, we can ride on the impetus it fires in us to aspire to greater experience than we currently enjoy and to lead our human nature back to our Godliness and God-like thoughts and abilities.

Loaves and Fishes (Matthew 15:14)
The famous Christian biblical parable of the loaves and fishes is a wonderful example of the duel between the solar plexus and the brow and eye centres. The solar plexus at one level measured a

hungry crowd and the little food that was the indisputable three-dimensional fact. Consequently, the energy of fear emerged and said, 'There really isn't enough to go around so we'll hang on to what we've got and the others can fend for themselves.'

However, Jesus knew that, by blessing the food (heart) and raising 'his eyes to heaven' (brow and eyes), he could take, through his heart and into his head, the need and desire to feed five thousand people. Through his higher, greater vision and perception of what was possible, the 'miracle' occurred and, by whatever means, there appeared enough food to feed the five thousand, and 'they collected the scraps remaining, twelve baskets full.'

In our healing process, our disease feeds upon the fear that concepts of limitation engender in us, and on the poor image we have of ourselves, and thus the poor view of what we can see ourselves achieving.

We have been given the most wonderful, creative imagination, with which we can achieve absolutely anything for ourselves and for others, as long as we dare to allow and nurture our higher vision, and foster in our mental selves those thoughts which will sustain it. This is the reason for our increasing belief in visualisation for achieving goals.

As the poem goes,

> *Two men looked out*
> *through their prison bars;*
> *The one saw mud,*
> *And the other stars.*

R. L. Stevenson

If we work with the mental connection between the solar plexus and the visual centres, we can heal ourselves and our lives easily, by replacing the old, limited diseased view with a vision of wholeness and unlimited possibilities, creating the reality we seek. Thoreau's maxim is perfect for this: 'Go confidently in the direction of your dreams: live the life you've imagined.'

Your imagination is not some accidental ability you are given in order to form pictures, so that you can have unattainable dreams, meaningless fantasies, and, perhaps, useful material for a bit of painting or writing. It is the working tool for the creation of your reality, and the improvement and healing of your life. In Chapter 3, I illustrate how, linking with the magnetic field, we create as we imagine, we can mould energy banks or substance into reality. All the great mystics practised this with sublime ease — Sai Baba, Christ and many others.

By bringing equilibrium into the dynamic relationship between the solar plexus and the head centres in the mental body, you clear a wonderful channel for healing and for the development of a life full of clear perception and open vision. You become a true visionary.

Signs that this centre link is poor are found in poor self-image, low self-esteem, and lack of hope and vision for the future, also in some aspects of feelings of undeservedness, unworthiness and a general feeling that life is huge, vast and imposing and we can do nothing about it — that we are dwarfed by its sheer magnitude.

Exercise 18 (B) — Integration of the Solar Plexus, Brow and Eye Centres

1. Relax and find the centre.
2. Connect with your solar plexus centre and the wonderful vortex of light within it. Symbolically, we imagine a clear, yellow light here.
3. Now focus upon the brow centre and, just beneath it, the centre between the eyes. These two vortices you can visualise as a deep violet and a bright purple respectively.

4. Allow three strands of clear, yellow light to flow upwards from your solar plexus centre, through your heart, into the purple and violet of the eye and brow centres. At the same time, three strands of purple and violet light flow down from these centres, again travelling through your heart centre, to your solar plexus. In this exercise, the links are established more fully between personal and universal spiritual vision, and your higher desires and real needs can be seen, imagined and realised. Think three times the affirmation: 'I see clearly now.'

5. After a few deep breaths, reflect upon the new balanced link you have made and the healing it is unfolding in you, before returning slowly to normal consciousness, connecting with the earth through your feet.

Root Base and Heart Centres — Will and Love

In the mental body, the root centre has its place in the focusing, in constructive ways, of our will and purpose. A properly balanced relationship between the root centre and the heart will unfold in a well-directed life and a clear sense of our own role unfolding perfectly within the general scheme of things.

However, we live in a time where most of us experience profound challenges. In the mental aura, which has a quite remarkable metallic-like glow in its colours, the malfunction of this relationship shows up more powerfully than most, with a dulling of the rays, especially the high rose ray, which helps us to think clearly about our relationships with others.

A clergyman came to see me on this very issue a few years ago. Over a brief period, I saw him several times, and developed a deep respect for the man. He was a good soul, very single-minded, and dedicated to his work and his parishioners, but some recent events had led him to become increasingly angry and, as a consequence, he was experiencing uncontrollable bursts of mental and emotional fury, causing problems with his stomach and digestion.

It was a classic case of what I refer to as a 'short-circuit', and the energy relationship between the root and base chakras and heart was being disrupted by a tendency to link them more with the solar plexus — with the attendant blown-up stomach and potential for ulcers, liver problems, nervous irritability and the precipitation of allergies, including asthma, the heart being by-passed in the normal counterbalancing in the chakra/centre system. This can also lead to heart problems.

Another phenomenon we experience when our will forces are not adequately balanced through the heart is our tendency to pad out our solar plexus with extra physical tissue in the stomach area, often through our over-eating and over-drinking, especially alcohol, so that we temporarily and superficially anaesthetise the area, allowing a brief and false calm. Whilst, in part, such can be the consequence of the energetic changes and challenges around us, as discussed earlier in this book, it is often also the result of misdirected will and the consequent mental weakness of such a tendency.

These tried and tested techniques will work wonders when considered and encouraged, enabling a more balanced and a clearer thinking process, putting us at ease and removing stress from the emotional body.

The clergyman found that the process helped enormously — he became more at ease with his work and the many demands made upon him by his parishioners, along with those of his own family. His stomach problems almost completely disappeared, and his recourse to a glass of gin became far less frequent and more recreational than therapeutic. He was able to express his love and compassion powerfully and gently, as he had always sought to do, but in a more detached and empathetic way than before.

Remember, the solar plexus holds us in sympathy with all the problems intimacy can provoke. As we take on the problems of others, we may be internalising their issues, their fears and difficulties, finding it hard to separate them from our own.

A good mental heart connection frees us from that, and our will flourishes through dynamic love and deep empathy, rather than emotional suffering and weak, ill-directed affection.

Exercise 18 (C) — Integration of Root, Base and Heart — Dynamic Goodwill, Love and Compassion

1. Take some slow, deep breathes and find your centre.
2. Focus upon your root and the base centres, using your imagination to see a range of deep red to vermilion light in them as they swirl, turn and pulse.
3. Consider your heart centre, a clear vortex, pulsing with bright, emerald green light.
4. Allow three strands of red light to flow upwards from the root centre, through the base of the spine and into the heart. As this happens, so the heart reciprocates, pouring three strands of green light down through the base centre into the root.
5. Personal and collective will harmonise, and the strength of your will-to-be, which keeps you incarnate and on the earth for this life's purpose, becomes integrated, revealing in you the will-to-good and the expression of love, giving and receiving unconditionally. 'My will works perfectly through Goodness' — think this, or say it, three times.
6. Retain these thoughts for a while, before returning to normal awareness, slowly and carefully as before. Make a further covenant with yourself, seeking out ways to give lovingly and freely to others. Small, heartfelt gifts and unsolicited services are perfect here, and anonymous ones even better. I

sometimes ask for a lecture fee to be given to someone or to an organisation, without revealing the source if possible. It is most empowering and encourages the integration we have just practised.

Also, develop your ability to receive. Accept gifts joyfully — I know many givers who are very bad receivers, yet, without the one, the other cannot find expression. All relationships are ultimately defined by the equilibrium or otherwise of such an exchange, and without it they flounder and, consequently, may die.

Solar Plexus to Heart — Fear to Love — From Personality to Higher Mind

Earlier, I mentioned the relationship between the solar plexus and heart vortices or centres, and the journey from fear and separation to love and belonging, but it is necessary to mention it again here, as it is a vital aspect of our mental healing, especially in these times.

Our politicians and leaders still, sadly, often wish to hold us in fear. They prefer it if we hold on to the old emotional way, hand over to them our power, and thus our responsibility, and cease to think clearly for ourselves. Our religious leaders are also a little responsible for this, asking us to trust their version of the truth, and not to debate issues. In these fast-changing times, this is no longer desirable or possible, as we wake up to the bigger picture and refuse to accept without question that which we are told. The fragment of rebelliousness in me which I have experienced over the years has had its useful side, and I could never do the work I do had I not been prepared to think freely and creatively, away from fear and limitation.

In the mental body, the heart is seeking to open doors for us, and always to align us to our souls and our intuition, so we cease to be re-active and, instead, become inner directed.

We must always operate through love, think through love, listen through love, speak through love, activating the resources of the heart chakra, and linking with the mind in our soul, clearing our fears as we do so. Whatever you do, and especially when you think, bring your heart into it.

The Silver Ray

When I was preparing my chromatic Flower Essences, I was told that I must try to capture the light of the silver/white ray for this purpose. Silver light has a wonderful frequency and links us to our integrated personality, marrying the male and female, and lifting our personality through our heart and higher mind towards our soul and spiritual selves.

It is interesting how we like to have this metallic effect around us, in our jewellery, our decorations, and even our cars, where a metallic effect in car-body paint is almost the norm these days.

Facing a shortage of silver flowers in my garden, I was led to the reflected light on the backs of certain leaves, especially the herbs, and also to the silvery white light of the full moon. At the time, the full moon was about to enter Aquarius, so I quickly arranged matters so that I could prepare it at that moment. I was faced with a cloudy night initially, but I prepared everything, and, magically, the magnificent silver-white moon appeared, radiating its light above the small pond in my garden, pouring its beams to exactly where I needed them. It was wonderfully empowering as I watched this special alchemy taking place in the still of the night. What my neighbours must have thought as I crept about my little moonlit garden, goodness only knows. But the magical silver light was captured, and it is used to good effect on myself and many clients, especially in the clearing of the relationship between the solar plexus and the heart, and the opening in us of the true, unconditional nature of our love.

Exercise 19 — Solar Plexus to Heart and the Silver Ray

Remember, our visualisations or imaginings take place on the edge of our three-dimensional reality, able to materialise any change we seek if we are loyal to them and diligent in our practice. What we make in our minds and fuel with good feeling can become our reality.

1. If you can, do this on a clear full moon, and it will be very powerful indeed. If not, enter your inner garden of light as before — after 'finding the centre', seek out your quiet place in the corner of the garden.
2. When you are there, allow the sun to set and the stars and moon to appear as the stillness descends. Enjoy the moment.
3. Observe the powerful, silver-white light of the moon shining down upon you, bringing its wonderful healing forces to you.
4. The silver light enters into every part of you, but especially the solar plexus and the heart, as both chakra vortices link together, sharing a wonderful exchange of the silver ray. It is gentle, yet profound, in its action upon you — heart and solar plexus working together.
5. As these lights merge, focus first upon your solar plexus, and reflect upon the blessing of being you — the remarkable fact of your individuality. As the light shines upon you, you radiate your own light and wisdom even more powerfully — you are unique and special.
6. Move across this bridge of sparkling light to your heart. Consider here how you belong to life, and how much you are a part of everything, and everything is a part of you. There is no fear in you, only joy and the radiance of love in your heart.
7. Bless the moon, thanking it first for its presence and the healing it will bring to you. And then leave your garden,

and, when appropriate, return to normal awareness, slowly and carefully as in the past.

After every healing exercise, we should say thank you and offer a blessing for the healing we are experiencing, for, whether or not we aware of it, some healing *always* takes place.

Dissolving Patterns

Tom had been diagnosed with cancer of the oesophagus; it was treatable but the prognosis was poor. As an individual who had nearly died once in his youth, he did not fear death, and actually, in some ways, welcomed it as the next part of his journey. An animated man of some spiritual persuasion, he decided to refuse the painful treatment he had been offered, which, at best, would probably only have delayed things a little and allowed him to sort out his affairs.

His family was, understandably, distressed, as there was an established pattern of different forms of cancer causing the demise of various relatives, including Tom's father and various aunts and uncles. His own brother had leukaemia.

One day, he had a vision. In a compelling set of images, he saw all those who had died of cancer looking at him as if he were the next in the queue. Suddenly, he gained the insight and connected with the thought stream that was to change everything. He realised that he didn't have to go down that route, and neither did his brother. There was a pattern here which he could break — and break it he would.

From that point on, and against all considered prognosis, his cancer went into remission. At the same time, his brother also had the same experience and was said to be clear of the leukaemia.

Tom's insight and consequent thinking had healed him and effected healing in his brother, breaking a pattern not only for

himself, but, it is to be hoped, for others. For, in the inter-
connected mental consciousness we all share, the quantum comes
into effect, and we can make breakthroughs in our thinking that
are real for everyone — initially within our sphere of influence,
but also beyond that out, outwards into the entire human family.

One client, Margaret, said to me about her chronic bad back,
'My mother had it, so I suppose it's my turn!' However, when
she decided that it wasn't compulsory for the sins of the fathers
(or in this case, mother) to be visited upon the children, her
healing began, and considerable improvements led to a disappearance of what had been a chronic problem. The only change
was in her thinking. By constructive thinking, and linking with
creative, unlimited thought streams, we can heal our minds and
our lives, and change anything we choose to.

A Reflection upon Patterns

~ *Think of the many layers of consciousness that help you to
express who you are — your physical and energy bodies, your
astral/emotional body, your mental body and your soul and
spiritual self.*

~ *Consider how each of these bodies and selves exists within the
plane of which it is a part, enabling you to function effectively
at that level.*

~ *Focus upon your mental body and how it flows in the plane of
the mind — a plane that is full of thought streams, ideas and
thinking patterns. You explore this level of yourself in a vast
sea of shimmering potential, in your own glowing mental body,
full of silvery, metallic colours and light.*

~ *In this plane, you can think as you wish, linking with any
thought patterns you choose. You can also release yourself from
any old, redundant patterns, just as you choose, and now is as
good a time as any to do that.*

~ *If a pattern comes to mind that limits you, and maybe also appears to limit those around you, let it go and see it drifting away from you, like a few loose circles floating away on a sea of light.*

You are ready to think afresh, to clear your mind of any old debris that limits you, enabling you to move forward to greater, more expansive ideas.

As Ralph Waldo Emerson said, 'The heredity you have is that which you believe in.'

Neil's Story

Neil was a high-flying financial consultant, working for a large banking institution. His job was to offer clients financial advice and to guide their investment and use of their money.

Neil had come to see me under extreme stress. The targets set for him were seemingly out of his reach, and he had been warned by his boss that they would be even higher the following year, and that his failure to meet them would place his future position at the bank in doubt.

We did some meditations to increase his energy levels and so reduce his stress, and we also began to look at his thinking. Neil felt that all the energy he was using, all the presentations he had done, were wasted, as he was developing no new business. Here was a pattern of thinking becoming fixed in his mind and, consequently, limiting what he could achieve.

The first truth we considered was that no energy, no effort, is ever wasted. Whatever we think and do will always bring its return. That is a universal principle — it is our 'casting of our bread upon the waters', which will always return, many times over.

It was also important that Neil used his power to be calm, yet determined to bring about change, to link with constructive and

expansive thought streams around him and not to be hemmed
in by his feared limits. He had appointments with prospective
clients later that day and some also the following morning. He
said that he would let me know how he fared, and he kept in
his mind the ideas that 'no energy is ever wasted' and 'I can
achieve what I need and wish to achieve.'

By Friday morning, Neil had had no success, but he called me
to say that he was keeping his focus and being constructive in his
thinking. Saturday arrived and the picture remained the same for
him. And then, on Sunday, at his home, he received a call. It was
someone he had advised six months previously but who, at the
time, had not pursued the service Neil offered to him.

The call was a revelation. The man had vast sums of money
to invest and had remembered Neil's sincerity and his thorough
approach in their meeting. He wished Neil to take him on as
a client. It was a wonderful breakthrough for Neil and he subsequently went from strength to strength, his sales figures flying
through the targets set for him.

Neil had always liked his job. Now he loved it, and was at
ease with it and himself.

Exercise 20 — Determination, Ease and Success

1. Relax for a few moments and find your centre.
2. Focus upon your root chakra vortex. Breathe deeply through
   it three times and feel the power in that centre. Be aware of
   the will and determination centred here, deep inside you.
   You can harness this force to link with the highest, most
   constructive thought patterns in the universe.
3. Draw this determination up into your heart and sense the
   ease in this chakra. This is the point of love, compassion and
   ease. Through your heart you can think and be as you
   choose.

4. Lift the forces of your determined, loving self upwards, into your head, beneath your crown centre. Focus here upon how that determination and the wise, loving ease of your heart, can enable you to link with the most elevated, expansive thought streams in creation.

5. Imagine these streams, flowing towards you in great waves of ideas and unlimited thinking. Blending these forces together, you can think as you choose, achieving and being anything you wish.

6. Be creative, focus upon new patterns, new success for you and your family and loved ones, and anyone you know. Hold the ideas in your head, one at a time, and then resolve to think and act accordingly, in the coming days, weeks and months ahead of you. Creative, constructive and unlimited thinking are yours. You can dissolve any pattern and change anything that you wish to change.

7. Bring your focus back to your heart and then, briefly, find your centre, before returning to normal awareness.

CHAPTER 6

THE SOUL, THE SPIRIT
AND HEALING

*The cure of a part should not be attempted without the treatment
of the whole. No attempt should be made to cure the body without
the soul ....*

Plato

Meditation

The world-famous musician, George Harrison, passed on to the
higher life whilst I was preparing this text, and to him, many in
the western world owe a great debt. He not only contributed
to some of the most definitive music of the 1960s and 1970s,
largely with his colleagues in the Beatles, but he also composed,
in his own right; and he, more than anyone, was responsible for
giving the Maharishi, his Transcendental Meditation technique
and, consequently, meditation in general, a high public profile,
the like of which could have been achieved only by someone
with his influence and significance in the popular consciousness
of the day. Since then, meditation has gradually filtered into the
cultures of the west, initially seen as a purely eastern spiritual
practice, though gradually re-discovered as a component of
Western Christian Mysticism, Hermeticism and, by some, ultimately as a quasi-medical tool for the relief of stress.

Some twenty years or more ago when I mentioned to my
GP that I practised and taught meditation, I watched his gaze
drop downwards to my feet to see whether I had begun to wear
sandals, and then move upwards to see if there were any brown

bean stains on my chin to confirm that I had joined the funny brigade. A shrug of the shoulders seemed almost obligatory, and a 'Well, if it works for you ...' usually followed, as the practice was dismissed as a cranky alternative to tranquillizers, sleeping pills, and the 'pull yourself together' stiff upper lip approach to life. I also recall that, in the early 1980s, a practising Christian who had a printing business refused to print the labels for my meditation cassettes in case they might be 'unchristian'. I had viewed this person as a friend.

I am glad to say that such unwelcome and ill-informed attitudes have largely disappeared, and meditation has been almost hijacked by the medical and healing professions as a significant aspect of ensuring mental and emotional health. Equally, there has been a renewed religious interest, which perceives meditation as a valid way of encountering whichever god is worshipped.

My own sons, currently 17 and 19 years old, have learned meditation with me at their request, the older one, Dominic, finding the practice particularly useful during his A-level exams last summer. In fact, over the past ten years, I have regularly taught meditational skills to young people, both individually and in groups, especially in two local senior schools. The young people respond very well to it and find the discipline most beneficial.

Meditation and Healing

Meditation is the highest aspect of our healing. The word itself has the same derivative stem as the word medical, and really means 'healing' or 'making whole'. Whilst we must be attentive to all the levels in us — physical/energetic, emotional and mental — and so nurture them, aware of what is happening to us at each of those levels, it is in our relationship to our spiritual light as revealed in our soul or higher-self nature that we find the core of our healing process. To neglect this results in healing methods

which, at best, may be little more than 'sticking plaster' therapy —
patching us up as we stumble from one state of disease to another.

The earlier pages of this book contain tried and tested
methods of working at these other levels of ourselves. I have
used these methods successfully over the years, but I have always
stressed, as my poor students will tell you, that meditation and
the spiritual journey have to be at the centre of any healing
process. If they are not, it is fixing, not healing. Moreover,
meditation is the ultimate spiritual journey.

Jane's Story

Through regular and consistent meditation, we embark upon a
process of growth and unfoldment that is irrevocable and quite
wonderful. It is a process that will change us and consequently
change our lives forever.

I remember a woman, Jane, who had come to see me some
years ago, initially for an aura assessment, but subsequently wishing to continue her unfoldment and healing with me as her aura
revealed not only her gifts and potential, but also one or two
impediments to her progress. As a part of this process, I worked
with her on some meditation exercises that I felt would help her,
and she made very good progress. She was an intelligent, determined individual, holding down a very senior position in the
local social services office.

One evening, I received a telephone call from Jane. She
wished to share her experience with me. For many years, she
had been travelling home from work along the same route, and
she was very familiar with it, or, at least, so she thought. On this
particular evening, however, something changed.

In rural East Anglia, where I live, the countryside is very flat
and, as a consequence, we have very broad, wide skies which
have intrigued artists for years as they stretch across the horizon
— huge, powerful and often dramatic.

That particular evening, we enjoyed a beautiful sunset, as the orange-red orb of light dissolved slowly behind the fields and trees. As Jane was driving home, she saw that sunset and the beautiful countryside in which it was framed, and it moved her deeply. She was reduced to tears, so much so that, at the earliest safe opportunity, she had to pull over in her car and pause for a while to enable this remarkable experience to wash through her completely. Jane found deep, remarkable healing as she sobbed with joy and wonder.

Jane had seen that view often — it was a stretch of road and countryside she passed through almost daily, and such sunsets are not unusual in clear Suffolk summer skies. But this was the first time she had really seen it. There was a new, deep connection inside her, and she was seeing now in a way she had never seen before. The effect upon her was profound and life-changing, and also very revealing. She now perceived life very differently. The familiar things were assuming a level of significance, meaning, and love that for her was transforming and healing.

'This is the first time I've really seen that road, those fields and that sky. It's like I was blind before — it was so beautiful, I was overwhelmed.'

Meditation does this for us. We are changed from an outer-directed, reactive being who takes everything for granted, rushing through life, never truly connecting with anything, to an inner-directed, awakening soul, looking from within at the glory of life — appreciative, with a new sense of belonging.

Jane's healing was not unusual. Another meditation student, having practised a technique for a month, complained that he had noticed no improvement or benefit whatsoever. He was bemused upon hearing that his wife and daughter felt that they were already 'living with a different man, calmer and happier than for years'. It was very early days and he had not noticed the changes others could see. But his healing was already underway.

Synchronicity, Magnetism and the Portcullis Effect

The healing our meditation gives to us is very profound and operates at all levels — from above to below, from within to without — through every layer of our being.

Carl Jung noticed that those who practise meditation of some type, and initiate the awakening of the soul which it brings to the individual, gradually find the emergence of a new, meaningful pattern to life, which was less apparent beforehand. He termed this 'synchronicity' — the sequences of meaningful coincidence whereby what we need in terms of people, opportunities, information, and even money, appear in front of us, as if by magic or convenient accident, just as we need them.

I recall a client who had taken up meditation as a therapeutic aid in the quest to stop smoking. He was a sales manager and spent many hours a day driving and, to alleviate the boredom, puffed away on cigarettes. Consequently, he was always coughing and unhealthy, and there was no point in his receiving healing help from me, or anyone else, unless he also gave up the dreaded weed. So, he was at least trying to. He had long dreamed of starting his own business but, as yet, hadn't found the way, and he thought that if he were more healthy and fit, he might be able to take the risk in the future.

However, one morning, the temptation was too great, and, on his journey to a customer, he called into a bar to buy a packet of cigarettes and take a break. He decided to have a coffee to accompany his cigarette. He didn't know the town or the bar but, oddly perhaps, he felt as if he should.

He struck up a casual conversation with another man in the bar who had also just popped in, to have a drink and a sandwich on his way to an interview — he had been made redundant some weeks earlier and was seeking a new job. He wanted to use some of his redundancy money to start an enterprise but was unsure about the marketing side of things, and he was still mulling the idea over in his mind.

That casual meeting blossomed into a friendship and a very successful business, marketing specialist golf accessories all over the world.

That is synchronicity — the texture and strands of our lives weaving together in remarkable, meaningful and, often, un-expected ways. My client told me that he threw the rest of the cigarettes into the bin — I think I believe him!

When we meditate and open to our souls, true healing can take place — body, mind and soul — and we gradually become totally integrated. We develop a clear picture of life, see mean-ing where meaning did not exist before, and anything becomes possible. We open to the true light of the spirit so that we express again the idea, 'if thine eye be single, thy body will be full of light' (Luke 11: 34).

In such a way, we become spiritually magnetic, drawing to us what we need, when we need it, in a form we can recognise and accept. We become the centre to which all things come.

Meditation also has another effect. In such a process, we are stimulating the Law of Attraction — attracting both what we need and also the 'birds of a feather' who flock to us because we are of like mind. At the same time, there is a complementary repulsing which swings into action. This repulsing I call the portcullis effect, because, whilst not giving us total immunity from problems or preventing us from making any mistakes at all, it does steer us away from some of the huge errors of judgment that could in turn lead to our straying too far off the path we have begun to tread. Once we've started on this most significant healing process, we actually have to fight very hard to get off it. This can be explained by the portcullis effect: situations where an invisible gate slams down in front of us, often suddenly, stopping us in our tracks and cutting us off from a course of action, or an individual, with which or with whom it would not be in our best interests to engage.

In as much as our healing is ultimately a return to a spiritually guided and enlightened life, when, at last, our personality has begun to wake up to the truth, this can be seen as the spirit taking its opportunity, through the soul, to reel us in like a confused fish in a turbulent sea. The portcullis is the soul's way of persuading us not to dither or be side-tracked by tempting, yet irrelevant or less important patterns, when a higher purpose has called us.

A Reflection

~ *Pause for a moment and take time to reflect upon your healing, your journey into peace and ease.*

~ *Consider the marvellous dynamic within you as the spirit seeks to work through your soul and your mind, enabling your personal self to be healed and connected to life in the most wonderful, purposeful way.*

~ *Think for a moment of those wonderful moments — for we all have some — when the strands of life interweave, providing for us those meaningful coincidences — perhaps seemingly miraculous, sometimes surprising — that thread everything together, providing us with opportunity, growth, healing and success. Consider both the greater ones and the smaller ones: they are all important and the more you consider them, the more they will seem to occur in the future. Say a thank you for them.*

~ *Let your mind also focus upon the times when the 'portcullis effect' deflected you from what, in retrospect, could have been a painful, or even disastrous experience, perhaps taking you away from some apparently great opportunities which might have placed your well-being in peril. This is the soul intervening, drawing you close to that state of grace where higher purpose begins to over-ride temporary, mundane and perhaps less important distractions. Say another thank you for that guidance.*

Stages of Meditation

We begin to approach meditation when we are engaged in life at many of its levels. Painting, drawing, singing, walking, gardening and jogging could all be said to be activities in which we may enter some occasionally spontaneous reverie or altered state that is, of itself, very meditative in its quality. I once attended a 'walking meditation' workshop, which was somewhat marred for me when my altered state led me to become rather less attentive to mundane things and I trod in something unexpected. My synchronicity rather let me down there, or perhaps it didn't — maybe I needed the experience!

However, we all need those quieter moments where we follow the inner way and seek the stillness and its deep healing. The exercise of finding the centre is a good beginning and one that I always teach in some form or another to students, clients and patients alike, whatever the reason for their visit. I sometimes hear people refer to a 'healing meditation' and, whilst I understand what they mean, I believe that it is, perhaps, an error in thinking. All true meditation is a healing act — the visualisations in earlier chapters are specific exercises with a meditative element, but they are specific and somewhat localised around a particular aspect of our healing. Meditation is essentially open and non-specific, and affects everything in our lives, so here we may consider the stages and a basic approach we might use.

The Pattern of Meditation

We commence our meditation and healing with ASPIRATION. We aspire to a better life, realising that to make it so, the greatest resource we have is ourselves. This is fundamentally important in all healing — therapies and therapists help us, but the process occurs in us and through us, not to us.

The trigger may be physical disease, excessive stress, phobia, or a desire to give up smoking or drinking, or to lose weight, or simply to find a meaning — an unrecognised prompting at the centre of all our disease, for healing, as it takes place, will always reveal meaning to us, little by little.

Aspiration takes us to the point where we wish to do something about our problem, our dis-ease, however it manifests and urges us to become active, maybe taking control.

Ben, a young lad of fourteen, was brought to see me by his mother, on a referral from another therapist. He experienced a whole range of problems which were, frankly, baffling most doctors. Ben had begun to endure states of anxiety and depression, along with extreme psychic states in which he heard voices, saw discarnate entities and felt as if he were going mad. It seemed, at times, that his life went out of control. In conjunction with this, he would also experience sudden eruptions on his face — spots and terrible acne-like manifestations. He couldn't cope with school and, although allergies and so on had been detected and treated, the problems still persisted.

My treatment of him involved the use of my Chromatic Flower Essences and some direct hand healing but, perhaps most important in his case, I also taught him a simple meditational technique, the first part of which was based upon our 'Finding the Centre' exercise. After one session, the improvement was remarkable. He still had problems, but they were far less severe and, more significantly, the regular practice of the meditation I had taught him helped him to feel, for the first time, that he was 'in control' of his situation — he felt that he had a strategy he could use that was central to his healing.

His mother and his therapist felt that Ben's condition was the result of a toxicity problem arising from an ageing, large natural-gas terminal near to his home. This is unproven, but, in my view, highly likely. Ben is well on the road to recovery, and the improvement is little short of remarkable. Your 'aspiration' included reading this book, or at least, this chapter.

RELAXATION and CONCENTRATION form the next component in meditation and, as such, begin the process of lifting our focus from the physical world, through the energetic and emotional, to the mental. One old psychic I knew used to call this part 'beating a path through the astral (plane)'. Here, we learn the techniques often associated with breath control, as in yoga and Qui Gong — techniques which remove tensions, slow down our metabolism and induce a sense of calm.

This part requires concentration and a resolve to continue to work at this process, whatever thoughts stray into our minds. For most of us, this is often the most difficult element in the whole journey because we live in a world where we are bombarded with mental forms and ideas, and generally encouraged to try to spread our thinking and do as many things as we can at the same time, often doing none of them as effectively as we might. Thus, the concrete mind resists the quietening down and one-pointedness that meditation requires of us, and it will try to jump around like a grasshopper in the wind.

In mantra meditation, we choose a word or maybe a phrase to chant or repeat as we seek to narrow our thinking down and concentrate upon one idea or thought, rather than the legion of issues that invade our minds, seemingly at random.

A mantra is a 'sound with power', although any word can be used. Many ritual prayer forms use mantra, sometimes linked to prayer beads such as the Catholic rosary, where the repetition of a spiritual idea or phrase is practised, in a rhythmic sequence. Eventually, in such an approach, the rhythm becomes more significant than the word, as we drift inward and upwards into our minds.

Along with mantra, we can also adopt a visual focus for concentration. Mandala and icons are a part of this tradition, but we can use anything — pictures, symbols, flowers or just colours.

We have to use our will to return to the process, when our mind plays tricks and wanders off to think about other things — 'Did I turn the oven off?', 'Have I booked my airline ticket?', 'I must go to visit ...' and so on. The beginning of meditation is concentration, an act of will, requiring persistence, but the persistence will eventually bring its reward.

There are not many things in life for which I would write a guarantee, but I would guarantee that, in meditation and healing, persistence will always triumph. Our relaxation and concentration exercise, in whatever form, will pay off and will calm us down more and more each time we work with it, giving us clarity and, progressively, easier access to our soul and our vast, powerful, spiritual world.

If you have worked with some of the exercises from earlier in the book, you will, no doubt, find this process much simpler, as you will have eased emotional tensions and already begun to clear your thinking considerably.

Once we have mastered this, we enter the process of true MEDITATION, where the words, images or sounds we are using take us deeply within ourselves, and our thoughts start to emerge from deep inside us, rather than from without, as reactions to our three-dimensional experience and the thought streams that bombard us. We begin to touch higher levels of consciousness and move towards our higher minds and our souls — it is a highly creative state. Sometimes we hit 'the block' as it is often called — a sense that we are getting nowhere, seeing, feeling, hearing nothing. Just void and blank — we've hit an invisible wall.

However, these periods of blankness, or 'non-thinking' are not really that at all. They are indicative of something much more significant, for we are leaving behind the realm of 'psychic delights', whilst opening up other, deeper channels within ourselves, through which the abstract ideas from the soul will flow as we are ready and waiting patiently for them. Patience and gentle persistence are the keys to this state. For this is where we begin our true healing, in what is often referred to as 'the silence'.

It is not really silence, but rather a peacefulness, or at-one-ment with life, as our sense of separateness dissolves. This state is sometimes referred to as REALISATION or CONTEMPLATION — we have access to new ideas and inspirations; fears evaporate; and problem-solving takes place at a deep, subliminal level. Tests using EEG machines, recording the brain wave patterns of meditators, revealed a quietening of activity of the brain waves as the meditation progressed through the Alpha state into calmness, but, surprisingly perhaps, as the meditators' state deepened further, the machines indicated a sudden increase in brain activity. These new and unusual, very intense patterns are unlike the earlier ones revealed, yet the meditator remained calm and deeply relaxed. The research suggests that, in the deepest state of meditation, some special problem-solving is underway, promoting a great and remarkable healing. This is the Higher Mind taking control, in the ultimate act of letting go.

The final aspect of the meditation is THANKSGIVING or ADORATION, the unravelling of a new awareness, and the development of a trust in the process of life. A sense of gratitude surfaces in us, and we learn to cease resisting life, instead accepting it and simply being grateful for being — an inner amen. This peak may be brief, but in the timelessness of meditation, that is enough. We may have meditated for twenty to thirty minutes, but it seems relatively brief, just as our sleep may do, and, just like the spider Charlotte in the film version of E.B. White's delightful story *Charlotte's Web*, we feel 'grateful to be a part of life, if only for a little while'. A new relationship with life unfolds.

We go on to be inspired by what we have discovered in our meditation — by the enlightenment and healing — and life can never truly be the same again.

Meditation Practice

We should make space daily for our practice. It is rather like any learning experience — little and often is best as we open an investment account into which we pay our spiritual currency. The more regularly we save, the more we accumulate, except that in meditation it is the most wonderful exponential curve — bringing untold dividends by clearing the stresses and strains of life, and opening our hearts and minds to our spirit.

There are many techniques and we cannot deal with them all here, but I offer you a basic pattern that will work if you are resolute and faithful to it. .

Exercise 21 — Meditation Preparation

If you are entirely new to meditation, I suggest the following as a good place to begin:

1. Sit quietly, away from every conceivable distraction. Take a small, narrow candle and place a horizontal pencil mark on it just a little way down from the top, enough for about five minutes' burning. You'll get to know how long it takes for that amount of wax to burn down.
2. Light the candle and place it safely in front of you — a few feet away.
3. Resolve simply to watch the candle burn down to your mark, and, in that time, to do nothing. Let your mind roam free during this period, ensuring that wherever your thoughts or eyes may wander, you gently and firmly bring your attention back to the candle and the clear light of the flame.
4. When your five or so minutes have elapsed, extinguish the candle, spending another minute or so in the stillness, before continuing with your daily activity.

Try to do this at least twice a day, preferably in the morning and again during the evening. Don't miss a day. You are making an investment in yourself and your healing. Gradually, you can extend this time until you can do it for ten to fifteen minutes at a session. You will discover that sometimes, during the session, you can close your eyes and see the candle-light inside your head for a while. As you progress, you may find that you can do this for virtually the entire period of meditation. This practice alone will begin to lead you into the meditation process, as you become calmer, less stressed and aware that something wonderful is happening. It is healing.

Exercise 22 (A) — Simple Mantra Meditation

For this approach, we use a simple mantra meditation, the use of a word as the centre of concentration. In some traditions, the meaning behind the word is important — that is actually what mantra means. Krishnamurti felt that the word was immaterial and that we could use anything, even 'Coca-Cola'! I will make a suggestion here for you, but you can be creative and choose anything with which you feel comfortable.

1. As a preparation, find your centre, as in Exercise 5. You may still wish to light a candle — I still do often, whatever approach I use.
2. For your mantra, or sound, focus upon the word 'love', and imagine it written in a space around your heart.
3. Repeat the word slowly, at first quietly with your voice, but gradually internalising the sound until it becomes a gentle rhythmic whisper.
4. This is the beginning of your concentration as you work deeply inwards and upwards through your mental self and aura. Continue sounding the word and, if your attention wanders, remember that that is natural, especially in the early stages of meditation. Simply return to your heart and your mantra.

5. In the early stages of meditation, this will be enough, and when you feel that you have been in meditation for a sufficiently long period, slowly return to normal consciousness, after connecting with the earth through your feet and gradually focusing on the space around you before opening your eyes. You then open them slowly and return to normal consciousness. After all meditations, very briefly find the centre. You can do this for a few second with your eyes open.

Some key points here are:

1. There is no absolute for the duration of a meditation; it will vary from person to person, but most find that somewhere between twenty and thirty minutes will emerge as the most suitable. As part of your inner devotion and healing, you will find that a period that suits you perfectly will unfold, although some days your need may be greater than others, or the development at that time may be especially important, so you will enjoy a longer cycle than you usually do.
2. In the early days, avoid practising when you are really tired, so that you don't fall asleep. Once you are experienced, it is less likely to happen. Always sit quietly, rather than lying down, if possible, but be comfortable.
3. Return from meditation as slowly as possible, always taking time at the end to pray. In my experience, those who return slowly from the deepened state of consciousness they have experienced derive most benefit from it. Eventually, you will not wish to rush back into everyday awareness, as the energy that meditation releases makes its impact upon you
4. Avoid eating just before practising as your stomach and solar plexus will hold you back like a ball and chain. If you are hungry, drink a little water and fruit juice.

5. Meditation is not sleep. We do not become so laid back that we float around in life, cloud-like, soft and ineffective. On the contrary, meditation will bring to us a heightened awareness — a sense of belonging, the likes of which we have never experienced before. Meditation heals us and wakes us up!

The Sleepy Fireman

Some years ago, I ran a course for the Fire Brigade on stress management and, as a part of it, I taught meditation techniques. Before the session, the head of the fire service took me to one side. He had a slightly troubled look on his face. 'This won't make them all too laid back, will it?' he enquired. 'Only, when that alarm rings, I need them on those engines and off to the fire as quick as possible — I don't want them so relaxed that they don't hurry and lose their sense of urgency!'

I don't know what he thought I was going to teach them, but the thought of these very manly, strong fire-fighters being so chilled out that they would react with incredible tardiness whilst someone's house was aflame did bring a smile across my face.

I reassured him that relaxed, unstressed meditating firemen would be ultra-alert and efficient, less prone to error and accident. I think he was reassured.

Prayer

Prayer is really focused, connected thinking, usually of high ideals; it is also petitionary, but often in some healing connection. At the end of meditation, we are 'attuned' like a fine radio, and therefore can transmit with greater efficiency. So, at this point, you first of all accept your own healing. Be in touch with the various levels of yourself, your mind, emotions, energy and body. Imagine the healing from the universe pouring through you, finding its way through all the levels of your being into the cells of your physical body. They will be 'enlightened' and in a healing process now.

Prayer is essentially an affirmation of the ideal within us and within our world, so we should pray for ourselves and those around us.

When we pray, we should imagine those who are the focus of our prayers experiencing their own healing — in their minds, their physical bodies and in their lives and affairs.

In this powerful time, it is perfect for us to work further upon our forgiveness, and also the bringing of health and prosperity into our lives, knowing that 'it is the Father's (universe) good pleasure to give us the Kingdom (everything).'

At the end of my meditations, I pray first for myself, then for my family, then friends, then neighbours, and finally for the world. I also do my distant or mental healing.

Remember — MEDITATION is attunement, the allowing of integration with our souls and the healing that it will bring. PRAYER is our creative involvement in that process and our opportunity to do something for others also. The earlier visualisations in this book are an aspect of prayer or devotional thinking — devoted to an idea or principle. And prayer does work. A recent experiment in a South Korean hospital showed how those in a group of patients receiving surgery benefited from prayer, as they recovered significantly quicker from their operations than a comparable group who were not prayed for at all.

When you pray for the healing of another, or indeed of yourself, always be confident — confident really means 'with faith' — and have images in your mind of an outcome of healing in yourself and in others. We pray not for the removal of disease, but rather for the unfolding and establishment of ease and health within us. There is a subtle, but important difference.

Exercise 22 (B) — Further Mantra Meditation

1. If you felt the mantra approach was appropriate for you, continue with it, starting as before in part (A).

2. Now, begin to lift your attention upwards from your heart, slowly repeating the mantra as you do, until your attention is focused in the centre of your head, level with your brow and your brow chakra.

3. Continue to sound the mantra, inside your head, until the word merges into a continuous stream of sound and vibration. The word will lose its shape, becoming a wall of silent sound. It may take some time before you realise that this is happening. When it does, allow the magnetic pull inside you to guide you. (This occurs in all meditation as the two hemispheres of the brain synchronise and a feeling of unity descends about you.) A doorway is opening to your higher mind and soul. The moments of apparent blackness that follow will be a sign that the mantra is doing its job, lifting you deeper inside and through into the light of your spirit.

4. When you are aware that you are not sounding your mantra, return to it, in the space in your head.

5. When you are ready, draw your meditation slowly to a close, as before, briefly finding your centre.

Exercise 22 (C) — Visual Meditation
Place before you some flowers or a simple, beautiful picture or image.

1. Find your centre.
2. Focus your attention upon the flowers or image you have chosen.
3. Study the flowers or image, as if you will have to describe them from memory later on. Consider the forms and shapes, the spaces between them, the colours and textures you see.
4. Allow your attention to find for you a focal point — a particular blossom, shape or image. Your mind will quite naturally do this for you if you ask it to.

5. Reflect upon the energy, the life force supporting the flower, or image, and how that energy has helped it to grow from a small seed, or idea. Close your eyes, taking the image inside you as you did with the candle exercise.
6. Imagine that you are painting the image inside your mind — the image may well change and develop as you do this. That is good and normal.
7. Eventually, you will begin to link with what is behind the image, or flower — the soul or spiritual essence from which it came, and from which all things come. This will emerge from inside you, as the 'blank spaces' you experience are allowing the thoughts to come from deep within you: your soul is beginning to develop a dialogue with you.
8. After a while, return slowly, connecting with the earth, opening your eyes slowly as before, and re-adjusting to everyday awareness.

You can develop visual meditation in many ways. Using the chakra drawing you produced earlier or by producing a special drawing — a pattern especially — is a good idea. This can then be the visual focus for your inner-healing journey.

Exercise 22 (D) — Colour Meditation
A simple colour meditation is an excellent approach to the inner healing journey.

1. Find the centre as before.
2. Think of the colours of the rainbow, through red, orange, yellow, green, blue, turquoise, indigo and purple, to violet. In the early sessions, you may wish to have some colour swatches with you to focus upon.
3. Focus on each colour as if it were a coloured stepping stone. Start with red, dwelling on it for a moment before moving

on to orange light. Follow this process gradually until you reach violet.

4. As you focus on the violet light, imagine all the colours coming together in a circle, like patches on an inner palette. Allow them to merge until you have in your head beautiful, clear, white, gold light. This is now your visual focus. Stay with this for the duration of your meditation before returning, as before, grounding and awakening slowly.

There are many approaches to meditation. I have offered here a few of those I teach, but all of them will lead you back to your soul and its healing. Persistence is the key. Those who persist will succeed, as with all healing activity.

The Soul Journey and Relationships

Meditation awakens us to the soul world from which we come. The soul is an individualised spirit — a piece of the creative source of the universe, expressing through you and each individual.

Souls exist in groups or families, and in your life here you will encounter many individuals who are members of those to which you belong. Your own close family and friends and those influential in your life are almost certainly members of your own soul group.

In your daily life, when you meet a member of your soul family, the magnetic attraction is all the greater and, therefore, the compelling desire to interact with them may, at times, be overwhelming, although that doesn't mean that you will always like them or find them easy to get along with. However, they will know, at least at a subliminal, subconscious level, why they are in your life and what role they have to play for you. The eyes, which express the dynamics of the soul, seeing its world and all within it, through love and wisdom, are a great clue here, for when we truly look into someone's eyes, and pause whilst doing so, we establish a deeper mode of seeing. The eyes function as the windows they really are, and reveal the more profound messages in our encounters and meetings. Often you will notice a twinkle in the eye, and a glow, or radiance — a sense of message, silently communicated to you, read and understood by your own inner self.

Eye Contact

When in doubt in a relationship or friendship, when puzzled, uncertain, bewildered or anxious about someone's role in your life, look into their eyes when you next meet them. Avoid staring, as that may intimidate or irritate them. But when you speak to them or meet them, look at them consciously for a few seconds. Be aware of looking at them through the forces of love and wisdom, so that you will understand, in time at least, who they really are and what it is you have to share with them. Imagine the link with them from your heart to their heart, from your higher mind to theirs — soul to soul.

Often, such a recognition is enough to change the relationship, or even promote healing within it, perhaps to allow it to slip away if its work is done. Whatever happens, you will have made a deeper contact with them, and understanding will come, not only for you, but also for them. No spiritual activity is ever selfish, or isolated — it is always communal or mutual, and any attempt to promote understanding and the healing that affords is a truly soul-based activity.

The person is probably a member of your soul family and is therefore crucial in the unfolding of your purpose, and hence its meaning in this lifetime.

The Soul, Relationships and Healing

Your Cause and Effect or Karmic Roll pattern will, for this lifetime at least, have brought you into dynamic contact with

some interesting souls, manifesting through their various personalities. They will have chosen forms that suit their needs perfectly
— having a birth time and date that will endow them with the
ideal astrological profile and enabling them to attract the perfect
energy and matter for this life. Their chakra system is programmed
like a set of cogs and wheels in a complex machine, so that they
may absorb and process the ideal blend of light and energy for
all the experiences they will have. That is also true for you.

And those souls whom you most need to encounter in the
physical world are here with you now. Some will have passed
out of your life, into new experiences of their own, either in this
world, or, in some cases, in new worlds after death. Others have
yet to cross your path. It is important to welcome them all and
allow them the honour and respect they deserve, however you
may feel about them at times.

To understand and bring clarity and healing into your
relationships, the following exercise is a very useful one. I use it
often in workshops.

Exercise 23 — The Relationship Circle

1. On a piece of paper, draw a large circle. In the centre, write
   your own name. This circle represents your immediate life
   here at this time, and you, of course, are in the centre.
2. Relax for a moment, and think of all the people in your life
   who are important to you, starting with family, friends and
   colleagues. If you have a large family and a huge circle of
   friends and close colleagues, you may need to do a separate
   circle for each group.
3. Imagine for a moment that you are in the centre of your
   circle, and these people are all around you; the ones you perceive to be the most significant will be placed closest to you
   in your circle, the others will be nearer to the edge.

4. Now draw a small dot or circle for each individual, inside your own circle, at the distance from you in the centre that you feel is correct and appropriate (see Figure 6.1). Use a pencil for this initially.

Figure 6.1: Soul relationship circle example

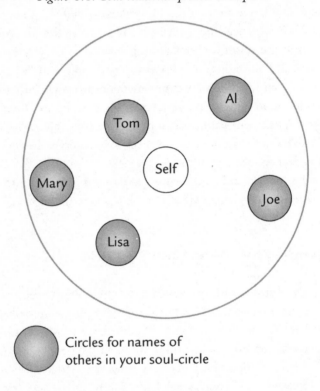

Circles for names of others in your soul-circle

5. When you have completed your diagram, study it for a while. It may be that you wish to change the position of some of the circles a little. You may even wish to remove some or add one you have forgotten. When you are satisfied with your plan, you can 'ink in' the names and circles.

6. Imagine yourself to be in the centre of this circle, with everyone around you. Slowly look around at them, seeing the light in their eyes clearly. They also have the power to look at life through love and wisdom, as you do.

7. Now, just as if you have wings, you can rise up, slowly, in the centre, so that you can look down on the circle and those within it. As you look around and study the group, you will begin to see things from a different, higher and clearer perspective. It is important to remember here that these people are knowing souls, part of your soul family, and are with you to help you to understand yourself and understand your life. They can help you to realise your potential.

8. Think of them all, connected as they are to the beautiful light of their souls, wonderful streams of light reaching upwards through the rays in their crown chakra vortex. And you also — you have such a connection with your soul or higher self.

9. From your heart chakra, flowing to all these individuals, are cords of light, which you have connected to them over the months, weeks and years you have known them. Through these cords, you can understand why they are in your life. Ask each individual and the revelation will come — not immediately perhaps, but in good time it will.

10. Give a blessing to each one, through your heart, and then thank them for being there, whatever their purpose for you. Again, recognise the soul and spirit of their true nature.

11. Come back down into the centre, connecting your feet with the earth, and gradually return to normal awareness.

Practised over a period of time, this exercise will promote a deepening sense of purpose and a vision of meaningful structures in your life. It will allow deep healing and a quality of recognition in your relationships which you may never have thought possible.

It is good, after such an exercise, to discuss with someone close the developments and insights. If you have a counsellor or good therapist, they may do it with you, or a good trusted friend. This is most useful as it speeds the release of redundant connections and relationships, whilst also providing the space for a fresh view of other soul and personality links which will come along in your life. Remember also to include in your prayer life all those you have contact with, or who are in your life.

Déjà Vu and Old Souls

In the human aura, it is increasingly common for me to see a particularly beautiful amethyst/purple light, which is usually to be found in the top half of the oval, usually near to the head. It is a colour that radiates from the soul, through the mental and emotional bodies, and expresses itself in our personality in various ways — most often as an underlying sense of destiny, a current of gentle restlessness that urges us to uncover the real reason for our life, the great things to which we often aspire, usually in the service of others.

This is the 'old soul' indicator. Many people speak of old souls, but rarely clarify what it is they mean or the significance of such an idea. An 'old soul' is a being who has travelled widely around the universe, experiencing diverse realities in many dimensions, and who may have a particular link with this planet, having incarnated here many times. I say 'may have', as the latter is not always the case.

There are common patterns of experience for old souls. They often dedicate their lives selflessly to the common good, are usually aware, to some extent at least, of the spiritual dimension of life, and sometimes the first half of their lives may be dictated by the needs of an ordinary, mundane or simple existence, only for them to awaken later on to the higher calling they have. I see this frequently in the province of healing and therapeutics, especially when such a career is embarked upon in middle age, when the children have grown up, perhaps, and our more mundane responsibilities may have lightened and changed.

Perhaps the most significant indicator of this is in '*déjà vu*' experiences, prophetic dreams, and an uncanny intermittent connection with life, where we seem completely and unusually familiar with everything around us. The *déjà vu* experiences most often occur when we are in a strange kind of detachment, watching what is going on around us with the distinct knowing that we have 'done that before'. This can be in a relatively ordinary situation — washing up, chatting to friends, or going to work.

Equally, the old soul will visit a new town or place and know it immediately, as if it were an old haunt or location they had visited many times before. It may also be that an individual you have just met, or someone you have known for some time, takes on a brief familiarity, far deeper than any you have experienced before. I was once watching a film based upon the life of a great reformer at the time of the Reformation in Europe. I was a very young boy, but the whole story had an unusual familiarity to it, especially when they showed sequences of the city in which he lived and worked. I also found myself disagreeing with some aspects of the story, saying, 'It wasn't like that!' several times. I had never studied that particular story or piece of history, but I knew the story and city well!

During a conversation we had recently, a client of mine suddenly exclaimed, 'I've done this ... this isn't the first time. I've seen it all before — every detail, even you lifting your pen as you did.'

Prophetic dreams are another indicator. The week before the 11 September World Trade Center disaster in New York, my 25-year-old daughter dreamt, on two consecutive nights, of a jet airliner crashing into two tall buildings. The following week, it happened. Although she had seen a preview, my daughter had had no idea of the actual situation or location until it happened. Of course, she was shocked and puzzled. She asked me why this had happened (as it happens to her from time to time) when she could do nothing to prevent it.

The experience was telling her something about herself — her nature — and trying to awaken her a little more to her soul nature, and to her importance, especially in this lifetime, as an old soul.

Soul — The Story

Before we incarnate and are born into this life, we know the destiny we have — the great possibilities that lie before us if we connect with our souls and grow towards our potential. We are given a preview of the life to come, with all its options and variations. As we encounter it, deep within us we know what is there for us, and sometimes recognise it, most powerfully in our moments of *déjà vu*, when we recall having 'already seen' the option in the pattern we are living out, and other people participating in it with us. A notion of pattern emerges, life begins to reveal a structure into which we may fit with increasing ease, if we allow ourselves to do so.

Most of us here at this time are old souls. In this crucial period in human unfoldment, vast numbers of souls are here to participate in the changes and, it is to be hoped, to assist in the healing necessary in all human beings, for we all need healing in some way or another, at some level or another. The world won't become overpopulated — even most demographic experts believe that the population here on earth is probably peaking and will begin to fall off this century. I agree, even if it means higher infertility levels, already showing in the west, to ensure that we get the pattern right!

You are probably an old soul, so your healing process should come as second nature to you. You are ready for it. However your disease manifests, it is a symptom of an awakening soul.

The Higher Circuits

As you progress with meditational activity and seek both to understand and to unfold the healing relationship with your soul and your spiritual being, you develop a new series of connections.

The progression is to Grace — that creative, powerful state of being — as the universal or divine within us awakens from its long slumber. These connections are the Higher Circuits, the meaningful patterns behind the three-dimensional world.

We have made great progress as we stop blaming others for our misfortune, or the vicissitudes of life for our disease. We no longer consider illness as purely physical symptoms, but rather see our diseases as elements of an accepted limitation, in our minds, emotional selves and energy bodies, which inhibit the free flow of the real self, that soul/higher self/spiritual creature which lies behind our manifestation. And its call is becoming ever more compelling as we recognise that we (the real we) are our own greatest resources. Others may help, and they often do, but it is the splendour within that we begin to glimpse and recognise.

These higher circuits call us to search for our destiny, to connect with the angelic realms, to understand the myth of death and know that there is only life. Healing is no longer a curing of disease, but rather a regaining of ease, attained through an inner (soul)-directed life, based on awareness and vision, wisdom and love.

Intuition and Inner Light

Ron told me that he never really understood why he had commenced meditation. He was rather over-stressed, holding down a job as a depot manager for a delivery company. Having taken various medications, he saw in a local newspaper an advert for a meditation course. It was quite an alien concept for him. He was a very down-to-earth chap, bringing up his family, preoccupied with paying off his mortgage and general survival, as most of us are. He wasn't especially ambitious or spiritually orientated. However, he decided that he would try this 'mystical thing', as he called it.

He did notice that he became gradually calmer, and his relationships improved — especially with his wife, with whom things had been a little strained and cool for some years. Ron had been experiencing periodic impotence and that also improved.

However, it was only after some years had passed that he was able to view the major impacts. He grew to see that, from the commencement of his meditation, a pattern had emerged and, although his life wasn't problem-free, it had certainly become less fragmented. Things had begun to fit together, and he could see very clearly the route he had followed.

People had appeared as he needed them. Perhaps more significantly, he had often been where he was needed, when he was needed. He said that it was like a jigsaw puzzle slotting together perfectly, piece by piece, with remarkable accuracy.

His physical health had improved considerably, his asthma virtually disappearing, and his reading matter had moved from detective novels to art, history, philosophy and esoteric wisdom. His career changed — he was made redundant, and an offer of a fresh job, with training and a role more suited to his quiet manner, came along almost immediately, like magic. His life was flowering — he was flowing with the universe.

Ron also said that he had become increasingly conscious of an inner guidance — not a voice or anything of that kind, but rather a sense of what he should do, and also the patience to wait, when things weren't clear, so that situations could develop and opportunities arise.

He had learned to trust. And trust indicates that we are living an inner-directed life and that we know we are. The shift for many of us to soul-based living is well underway, as it was with Ron. Stress was no longer the issue for him — life was. The intuition is the voice of the soul directing us from within. Intuition means 'inner teaching' or 'to be taught from within'. We are first inspired by our new-found vision of what is possible for us as our deepening relationship with our soul heightens our awareness of life around us. Ultimately, our heart and head combine (pineal gland and heart centre) to help us to understand the message we are receiving, to interpret effectively, so that we can see what we have to do. We may then act upon it. The more we trust this process, the more it works for us.

However, on our healing journey, our destiny unfolds with even more clarity. Our soul seeks to build a permanent, perfect, long-term vision for us, inside our minds, in the link between our soul (pineal) and mental (pituitary) selves. We are being guided from the highest levels.

Enlightenment

Each time we meditate, the soul places in our minds a particle of a great thought or idea. It does this gradually, as we are able to cope with it, piece by piece. Over the days and months, this thought form grows and gently magnetises us, in keeping with our highest good and supreme pathway, so that we may progress with increasing ease and clarity towards our greater purpose. There can be no greater healing than this.

As George Harrison said simply, 'We have to discover who we are, and why we are here.' He was absolutely right. This is the beginning of enlightenment, the formation of the 'light in the head' of the esotericist and mystic — the tongues of flame on the disciples' heads at Whitsuntide. Such a formation is guided by the pineal gland. This magical gland, in the centre of the head, connects with the divine or universal light that comes to us through the crown chakra vortex, and, rather like an electrical sub-station, downloads it into our minds at a frequency and rate we can tolerate. Damaged pineal function causes many problems, including some forms of schizophrenia and psychotic behaviour, and generally weakens our imagination and vision, often manifesting as a very disorganised mind. In severe cases, we may experience problems with light itself, developing light-sensitive allergies and extreme photosensitivity.

Good pineal awakening is very necessary in our healing and enlightenment. As discussed in Chapter 2, many esoteric traditions support the idea that the fontanel — the soft area we have at birth at the top of the head— is the residual evidence of an earlier filter, and that we once were able to breathe directly through a channel in the head to the lungs, the breath energising the pineal gland on its journey. Also, as mentioned in Chapter 2, in times gone by, some parents of newly born babies would request that their children's heads be exposed to bright light soon after birth, so that the pineal gland would be stimulated and their children might remember their inner light and the realms of light from which they had come into this world.

Meditation and modern spiritual traditions circumvent this by mental processes, as we will do here.

Exercise 24 — The Soul's Light

1. Find your centre, as in Exercise 5.
2. Link with your heart centre: this is the seat of love and wisdom in you. Take three deep breaths here, reflecting on that idea as you do so.
3. Gradually lift your concentration up until you reach the inner space in your head, just behind your forehead, beneath the crown.
4. With your thoughts, affirm that you are ready to listen to your soul — your higher self. You are ready for direct soul

guidance in your life, to fulfil your own destiny here on earth, in keeping with the highest principles and needs. You will use your will to do good, for yourself, for life, and for everyone and everything within that life.

5. Focus on those ideas for a while. You may well find that a beautiful light or deep indescribable feeling of joy surfaces inside your mind and heart. Your heart has the map of your destiny, and the light that grows in you as your soul takes control will illumine that map clearly for you.

6. Gently bring your focus back to your heart, remembering to be 'in the centre'. Ground through your feet, and then return to normal consciousness slowly.

You have initiated a wonderful process. If you return to this meditation regularly — perhaps once a week to start with — you will change, grow and experience a developing, embracing sense of ease in every part of you — body, emotions, mind and soul.

Using the Exercises

There are many exercises in this book. Some will appeal to you more than others, or feel more appropriate for your needs. However, you will find that once you have practised an exercise for a while, it will become integrated into your mind, so that you can 'switch on' the idea or principle quickly and power-fully as your subconscious absorbs into its programming the new thinking and awareness. You can then move on to work with other ideas and exercises, occasionally referring back to the earlier ones if you wish. You will be surprised how far you have come and how much you will have changed.

The meditations in this chapter are examples of some daily, open (non-specific) meditations you can use on a daily basis for the rest of your life. These will develop as you do. This last meditation is a very special one — a surrender to the wisdom and the love of the universe in you, and its supreme intelligence, that it may guide you perfectly. An exercise of this kind should be practised regularly, alongside daily meditation. Remember, all meditations are healing.

Linking with Destiny

The cemetery is full of those who thought they were indispensable.

Somebody offered this weak and sadly inaccurate cliché when we were discussing hard work, stress and the ever shortening of time available to us as we struggle to cram into our days more and more activity.

Whilst it is true that, in the quickening we are experiencing during this transition of the ages, until around 2011 or so, we are faced with a burgeoning growth in our activity and the demands it makes upon us, we are perfectly equipped to deal with this.

We are never asked to do anything for which we are not equipped — life doesn't work in that way and a quick review of your life thus far will support that idea, however challenging and hard your life has been.

As I have said, the world is becoming less magnetic, and more electric, with the charges of ever-flowing electrical thoughts coursing through us and around us. The rotation of the planet is slowing, climate is altering dramatically and our current global economic pattern is unsustainable for much longer. We are confronted with vast changes on every side.

However, we are perfectly structured for our tasks, as long as we use everything we have, everything in our nature that is given to us. We must use our whole, healed nature — not just a part of it — to pursue our life. That is the holistic, healthy way. Then we can achieve anything.

And we are indispensable. The universe doesn't make spare or redundant parts. It has no need to do so. The parable of the lost sheep in the Christian gospels is a celebration of the indispensable value and unique quality of each of us. You are indispensable, because of your individuality and, in this life, at this time, it is your responsibility to exploit that as fully, as creatively and as wisely as you can.

Your life map and destiny are within you from the beginning, and you can unlock that map and co-operate with it.

The main components in our destiny ladder are:

~ *Purpose* — that channelling of individual will for both individual and collective good.
~ *Power* — the realisation and direction of energy to sustain us on our journey along the path.
~ *Need* — the fulfilling of that which is essential for us to experience, both through people and circumstances.
~ *Understanding* — the action of wisdom in us so that we may understand our purpose and its nature, pursuing it through our hearts and not just our minds.
~ *Self-expression* — the point of vocation or 'calling', which enables us to find the most appropriate channel(s) through which to work.
~ *Vision* — the recognition and vision of what is possible for us in life, how we can act and then measure our progress and effectiveness.

The last is most important, for we are blessed with the facility for very sophisticated remembering. In fact, we remember everything and we forget nothing. We may, for various reasons, lose some access to our memory, but it is always there, even when the brain is damaged, we are in shock, or we have clouded our mental body because of fears and anxieties at our emotional level.

Our capacity to recognise is quite a remarkable gift. Imagine if, for every visit to your town, you were starting from scratch and had no memory of where things were — shops, car parks, cinema, and so on. We would barely grow, developing very, very slowly as sentient beings. A frustrating visit to a local store, where the habit of changing the shelf location of the various goods for sale is the norm, illustrates the point effectively. We spend half our time looking afresh for everything because we don't know where it is.

Our magical vision helps us to recognise as information what we are being given, and subsequently to recognise how we can act upon it, recording, with the outer vision of our eyes, the effects of the actions we take in our world — a truly wonderful, blessed gift. Consider a world without your ability to remember anything. You would have no bank of experience upon which to build. Your destiny is in your hands, and the earlier meditations and practices in the book will doubtless have initiated moves in its awakening.

The following exercise will help you to link with that more dynamically.

Exercise 25 — The Simple Destiny Ladder

1. Find your centre.
2. Focus upon the centre at the root of your spine. This centre and the light in its vortices — energetic, emotional and mental — is the seat of your purpose. When you are born, the forces manifest here draw your soul into incarnation. Imagine here a funnel of beautiful, deep red light. Reflect for a few moments upon your *purpose* for this life, allowing thoughts to come and go as they will.
3. When you feel ready to move on, focus upon your heart centre. The light in the vortices here is symbolised by beautiful green rays. This is the seat of wise understanding of your path, the point at which purpose is given meaning. Dwell

here and focus your thought upon *understanding* your destiny. There is a map of destiny in your heart and, with sustained and gentle encouragement, it will reveal its message to you.

4. Again, when you feel ready, move your concentration to your eye and brow centres, where you link with vision and the power of your imagination to give form to your destiny in a way that you can recognise. In as much as destiny comes in instalments, your visions will be linked in series — one at a time, as you need them. Be patient and the vision will come to you, not necessarily immediately, but gradually. Maybe after your meditation, or in an odd, still moment, a picture will be given to you. Perhaps the vision will come, as mine often do, through the memory of a dream.

5. Finally, take your attention upwards to the crown chakra vortices, at the top of your head. As you do this, remember that you are connecting the constituent forces of your personality, integrated into your pituitary gland, with the inspiration of your soul and spirit as it pours through the crown and activates the pineal gland.

6. Imagine and sense the stream of light that links you via your own soul, out into the universe, and thence to everything within it. Reflect on the sublime nature of that truth and the healing that it brings to you, guiding you through your life. During each day, briefly reflect upon this idea in any moment of pause — over a cup of tea, whilst on a bus or train, wherever you can. Do it often.

7. Finally, imagine the light of your root centre as it links with the light in your heart and then the light in your head, threading all the strands in your path together as it does so. *Purpose* — Root Centre, *Power* — Abdomen, *Need* — Solar Plexus, *Understanding* — Heart Centre, *Self-expression and Calling* — Throat and Mouth Centres, *Vision and Recognition* — Head Centres.

8. Give thanks for your life and the blessing and opportunity that it gives to you, whatever problems you may have encountered and be encountering now. As your healing unfolds, so you will move on with greater ease and creativity. If you find that you are not yet able or willing to do this, do more work on your emotional and mental bodies, as in the earlier chapters, and come back to this again later.

9. In conclusion, bring your focus slowly back, briefly finding your centre, and then connecting with the earth through your feet.

This is a most important activity. I was once asked in a public lecture how we could use the aura to help in healing. In my reply, I explained how, if I could help someone to develop a sense of purpose, to catch a glimpse of their destiny, that was the greatest healing they could experience.

I Can't See Visions — I Have No Imagination!

This is a statement often uttered, and I understand the frustration that prompts it. On my courses, there are frequently souls who say that they do not see anything. The important idea here is to think through the pattern of the exercise. If you 'think' the exercise somewhere inside you, a picture will form. You may not see it to begin with but, with sufficient practice, it will gradually appear. In the meantime, while the pictures or vision are subliminal or invisible to your conscious mind, sense or feel what you are seeking to imagine.

In this way, you will develop a very strong feeling (not to be confused with emotion) — a sense of sure knowingness of what you are being told. This is the intuition in operation, talking to you from the depths of your being. You will learn to know what it is showing to you and saying to you.

Keep a spiritual journal for this and all practice. Insights and teaching will come to you at unexpected moments and, as you receive them, note them down, because, over a period of time, the pattern will emerge and your 'vision' will form for you.

One client who had attended a course of mine, where we explored the unfolding of individual destiny, rarely experienced visions. Her soul, however, found many ingenious ways of talking to her and showing to her the things that she needed to see. She would be browsing through a catalogue, or looking at picture postcards in a shop, when she would stumble across a picture which she knew, beyond all doubt, was speaking to her very specifically, guiding her.

It may be that you hear what you need to see, in a phrase of a conversation you overhear, or on a radio broadcast, where an idea leaps out at you, or you might even hear yourself saying to someone else something that you know is for you also! My clients are often amused, or even bewildered, when, both in workshops and at private appointments, I will suddenly recognise an important idea that arises in the teaching or advice I am giving at that moment, and I will frantically search around for my notepad to write it down quickly. 'I've just had an insight,' I'll say apologetically.

There is an important point here for all therapists, healers and teachers. We need our patients, clients or students as much as they need us. Not only do they give us a powerful opportunity to express our compassion and our zeal for sharing and service, but they also teach us. Gerry Jampolski implied that we teach that which we need to learn, and there is much merit in the idea, for I learn from every appointment I give and every course I tutor. The same is true for everyone.

So be vigilant and look out for the new messages and visions your soul gives to you, wherever you are and whatever you do. These exercises will encourage life to have a more meaningful dialogue with you. There is no point if we don't watch and listen, for it is largely our inattentiveness to life that leads us into disease in the first place.

The Group Destiny

Our own destiny is inextricably linked to that of our group — that of our earthly family, our demographic community and nation, our soul family and the entire human race on earth.

To be healed, we need to recognise our participation in the process of the group — the vast swathe of humanity, living together at this time upon the planet. From a spiritual perspective, we are all simply different versions of the same model — like motor cars, where, to promote the sale, the manufacturers may tweak with the details of a new model to make it more alluring and marketable, yet, fundamentally, it is the same vehicle, irrespective of colour and trim.

During your probable various incarnations upon the earth, you will doubtless have lived within most racial groups and subgroups, most types of society and most social strata, from rich influential man to impoverished beggar, male and female, black, white and yellow. You will almost certainly have tried most religions, from monotheistic ones such as Christianity, to the polytheism of Egypt. Such an understanding makes racial prejudice and religious bigotry look as absurd as they truly are, and makes social class and status irrelevant apart from what they teach us about ourselves and our reaction to such experience. The maxim, 'There but for the grace of God, go I', should be changed to, 'If I haven't already, then I probably will.'

In these times, many of us have chosen to incarnate together on the earth, to use our awareness and experience to heal ourselves and the human family. Most of us have forgotten that fact, but, increasingly over the next ten years, to 2011 or so, we will recall our true nature and heritage and see the current cultural, religious, economic and political structures in their true light, and the shallowness that lurks behind them. Only those who work with good motive, for the common good, are likely to survive the shake-up ahead without considerable stress and challenge, necessitating much healing. Greed, though rife, is, I feel, approaching its peak, along with all the other manifestations of selfishness which cause us so much disease as we seek to possess that which cannot be possessed and control what cannot be controlled.

Figure 6.2: Flow of souls

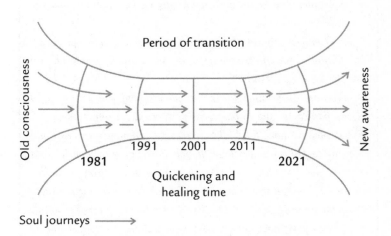

I remember clearing out my parents' bungalow after my father's death, my mother having passed on to the next life some months earlier. At first, as I surveyed the few possessions he had acquired over some 79 years, I felt a wave of sadness — there was so little to show for so many years of hard work and sacrifice. But I quickly realised that the truth was not in these things. The measure of the man and his soul, and the impact he had upon life was in the love he had for me, my sister, my wife and our children — the often selfless contribution he had made to our lives, enabling us to grow and to experience the things he had not been able to, during his hard and often difficult life. I remembered what mattered. To be healed, that is what we all must do.

Reflection

~ *Reflect for a moment upon the growth of population on the earth, especially in the past fifty to sixty years, as the number of souls incarnating together has grown, rapidly increasing the world's population.*

~ *Consider how we are all here together in these rapidly changing times.*

~ *Remember how we all share a common global destiny; we are all important and have a necessary and valuable role to play in the Human Destiny.*

~ *You are truly important in this process, and you are equipped to participate and to play your part, whatever comes along.*

~ *Remember how, by thinking as a soul, through your heart and mind, you can understand the role others play in your life and how they can help you along your path in life. You are linked to everyone in some way. In your heart you will recognise those who are truly significant for you — soul to soul, mind to mind.*

~ *When you understand yourself to be a soul — a spiritual being — everything changes and your liberation from disease is underway.*

Manipulation

As souls, living through our spiritual light, we become alive in the most wonderful sense. Perhaps the most notable aspect of our awakening is that we recognise that we ourselves are the cause of all the effects we experience in our lives, either by direct action or indirect action

Direct action can be linked to the ripples we make when we drop a pebble into a pool of water. They radiate outwards, touching everything in their path as they go. Out thoughts and actions have this direct effect upon us, our world and experience.

Indirect action is the effect we experience when the ripples hit the edge of the pool and then ricochet back towards us, ultimately reaching us in the centre where the pebble was initially dropped. On their way back, they encounter the fresh ripples and waves we have made. As they hit each other, there may be some turbulence, and those strong enough return right into the centre, and their effects, make us very aware of our initial direct actions. Things that may have been hovering on the edge of our lives, waiting to be stirred, are attracted to us in the centre.

We can make fresh, direct waves to keep them at bay, and even send them away again, dissipating them completely, but these have to be timed perfectly, and initiated and considered with a calm mind, governed by an awakened soul.

Awareness of this aspect of the Karmic Roll, is the beginning of Grace and freedom from what appears to be learning by accident or reaction. There are really no accidents in life, and as we become soul-aware, we realise this to be so. Everything results from a cause, and has a purpose. Remember, we should always ask, 'What is this experience showing to me/saying to me?' 'What is this person teaching me?'

Such a request is always answered in due course, and when the lesson is recognised and really understood, the circumstances or the individuals involved in our learning process disappear from our path. Recognition comes first, followed by understanding and then growth, change and healing.

I knew a woman once who had great problems with her neighbour. They had got along well in the past but their relationship had deteriorated, and my friend lived in a state of tension and anxiety, very unhappy that they could not discuss their issues and heal the situation. She was a good, sensitive soul and, soon after the commencement of the difficulties, she developed an inflammation in her mouth and throat, which did not respond to medical help.

Eventually, she recognised that her physical problem was the consequence of the situation. However, recognition did not heal the situation. 'I know what's causing it,' she said. 'But it still won't go away.' However, in the ensuing weeks, she began to understand more clearly why the conflict had arisen, and some of the deeper issues involved, not the least being that she didn't express her own viewpoint clearly. Once she understood that, her throat gradually healed, and the condition has never returned.

RECOGNITION > UNDERSTANDING > HEALING

One of the effects of our soul-based living and knowing ourselves as cause is the diminishing ability of the outer world both to control us and to affect us.

At a research institution in Odessa in the former Soviet Union, research by the secret services into mind-control techniques revealed that those who are naturally clairvoyant not only created a strong personal magnetic field to scan and influence the space around them, but they were also resistant to various kinds of artificially induced magnetic waves around them.

A natural, well-developed clairvoyant, when attuned via the pineal gland to the highest frequency light from the soul, which enters the system via the crown vortex or chakra, also develops a vortex of energy around them, which, in turn, makes them resistant to outside influence and control, apart from that which they choose to accept or focus upon. We will look at vortex theory a little more in a moment.

However, the truth of this idea is quite astounding. It means that, through meditation and soul connection, we as individuals remove ourselves from the normal controls and manipulations that are around all of us.

In his excellent book *The Hidden Persuaders*, Vance Packard explored the means by which advertisers try to persuade and manipulate human consciousness through subtle (and not so subtle) mind-control techniques, largely to influence our purchasing habits. More sinister motives are revealed in other research, which suggests that these techniques are widely studied by the secret service and military around the world.

The Three-Rhythm Technique

Politicians exploit them continually, especially using the 'three-rhythm technique'. This is the method whereby we repeat an idea, perhaps with slightly different words, three times, to influence and control the mind of the listener. An analysis of political speeches will soon reveal how widespread this is — I have made my children aware of this approach and encourage them to look for it. These techniques are linked to old magical practices where everything is done in threes. Freemasons clap in threes to affirm a speech or teaching; the genie offered Aladdin three wishes; military drumming was nearly always in threes, especially when accompanying a command to attack the enemy or obey an order; we start our races with 'Ready, steady, go!'; and how often in church were Catholics encouraged to feel more guilty than they already did by saying, '*Mea culpa, mea culpa, mea maxima culpa*'? (No wonder some of us get depressed.) The use of threes is simple — the first command or exhortation influences the conscious mind; the second penetrates into the subconscious — the conscious mind then having been loosened up; the third hits the superconscious or soul mind, and we are hooked like a fish on a line; wriggle though we may, it will take a big effort to break free.

As a society, we are surrounded by attempts at control — much more than we realise. American research documents reveal that one in five individuals can be hypnotised to such a depth that they will not remember afterwards what they have done whilst in the controlled state. That is the bad news.

The good news is that those who practise meditation regularly and are inner-directed are not hypnotisable at all. When you practise meditation and develop your soul link, as part of the healing, you gain complete control over yourself and your destiny. The hidden persuaders of any kind — commercial, political, religious or military — cannot touch you.

to mastery of life and outer experience

to discovery and self-mastery

through the awakening of self-awareness

we journey from disease

The Spirit and the Vortex

In the nineteenth century, leading physicists acknowledged the idea of an ether as being the most likely explanation for the nature of the invisible substance of the universe. Furthermore, the theory emerged of the vortex as the means by which energy travelled through this ether. Lord Kelvin believed that the atom was a vortex, as did other eminent scientists of the day, such as James Clerk Maxwell, founder of the Cavendish laboratory at Cambridge, and the discoverer of the electron. Sir John Thomson also espoused the idea of the vortex atom.

Sadly, the development of physics in the twentieth century, especially after Einstein, sought other, more complicated and reductionist theories, and moved away from the truth. Every time we think, we create a vortex. Some thought forms are completely spiral in form. To clairvoyant vision such as mine, energy and light move in spiral vortex forms, and in our subtle bodies, at the major points of activity, we have the chakra vortices. Our DNA likewise moves in a spiral and, in nature, the spiral vortex can widely be seen as still evident in physical expression — the tornado, the snail shell, the arrangements of cauliflower florets, and a double vortex in the sunflower. Our toes and finger tips also still reveal the vortex in the tissue formation where the chakra vortices there create our distinctive finger (or toe) prints.

The links between our dimensions are also vortices. The black holes of space are an early scientific recognition of this. Any experienced researching meditator and spiritual scientist will know that to travel through space and time, the last thing we need is a space ship. We can travel through space and time through vortices, and so our measurements through space based upon the speed of light are seriously flawed and irrelevant, for the matter revealed in vortex is outside the retinal visible spectrum and is not governed by our current limited physics of light.

When we meditate, we create around us a huge vortex. This vortex has two major effects. First, it produces a space, in which, drawing upon the energy banks mentioned earlier, we can bring into physical materialisation absolutely anything. In the centre of the vortex, energy becomes matter. Again, scientific and military research, in the US and former USSR amongst others, has been exploring this idea for many years. The researchers are aware that thought can not only move matter by telekinesis, it can also both form and disperse physical substance. Mystics and mediums have known this for a long time, and science is slowly, and perhaps rather reluctantly, catching up.

The second major effect is that the vortex acts as a shield or safe space, which makes the individual impervious to the uninvited thoughts, action and pollutants, both physical and superphysical, that abound in our environment (see Figure 6.3). Regular, deep meditation creates this vortex and holds it in place, so that we are no longer the victim of the outer world and subject to its demands or attempts at manipulation. We are truly in the centre.

Fi.gure 6.3: Primary force movement in vortex formation

We do not have to build this vortex consciously — it is a kind of gift from the soul, and is very visible in the mental bodies or aura of some individuals. The halo in renaissance paintings of religious figures is, in part at least, an allusion to this idea, for it forms most densely above the head, and then produces an expanding conical form downwards, to just below the level of our feet.

Within this space, not only is total healing possible, but eventually it becomes certain. You should, perhaps, reflect on this also, after your periods of meditation and before you use your thoughts for prayer and healing.

Angels, Souls and Healing

In Chapter 2, we considered the Solar Angel, the messenger of perfection within our nature. I have seen angels, from my earliest childhood, although they have rarely seemed to me to be the more anthropomorphic beings described by most people. For me, they were always like bright, metallic cones of light, not dissimilar to the vortices to which I have just referred, only more vivid and varied in colour.

Angels in all their forms — from the nature spirits and elementals, who hold nature in place, to the elevated Seraphim of Dionysius — are God's engineers. They work with the light in all its forms, as if it were a magic putty or moulding clay, ensuring that the laws of the universe are sustained and maintained. It is said, for example, that the highest angels, the Seraphim, look into the face of God and obey his thoughts by keeping his reality in place according to his divine will and image. Sir George Trevelyan referred to them as 'strands of thought in the mind of God'.

We cannot so easily effect our healing and open ourselves to our true spiritual nature unless we acknowledge these engineers, and co-operate with them. Our own Angelic Self, the Solar

Angel, gives us a reference point through which we can connect to this higher mental realm. And, from a healing perspective, the most important is the Angel of the Presence, sometimes referred to as the Body Elemental, or Healing Angel.

Angel of the Presence

The Angel of the Presence is the ever-present higher mental intelligence that links directly with our soul, through the perfection of our Solar Angel.

Its function is to express, out into the physical world, the quality of our soul and its spiritual nature, by means of our energy or etheric body. It understands completely the reason for this physical life and how best the physical body can be formed, nurtured and maintained for as long as physical life is useful and necessary. The etheric body is the soul's vehicle in the physical world, attracting to it the physical atoms to build its physical form. At death, it follows the dictate of the soul and prepares us for passing, in some cases through a vortex close to the heart, but in most situations through the crown centre.

A sustained recognition of the presence of this wonderful intelligence is to be encouraged as we grow into our healing, leaving our disease behind.

Exercise 26 — The Angel of the Presence

1. Find your centre as before.
2. Remember the Solar Angel, your soul's expression of its perfect nature.
3. Ask your Solar Angel to open your heart to the Angel of the Presence as it sustains your physical presence here on the earth.
4. Think of the etheric (energy) body and the physical body it forms and maintains for you in your daily life. As you do this,

be aware of a clear, translucent presence, seeking to govern this process perfectly for you. It does so in each moment of your incarnation, without your conscious intervention.

5. Thank the Angel of the Presence for its work on your behalf, becoming aware of your physical body as you do so. Notice your breathing. Consider the myriad remarkable physical functions being performed in you — all being directed by this being of light, in co-operation with your soul, your spiritual self. This is truly a wonderful realisation — rest in it for a while, before returning slowly to everyday three-dimensional awareness.

The Illusion of Death

It may appear strange to some to mention death in a book on healing, but it is because of our ignorance of the process that we fear it and refuse even to discuss it. Yet, it is something that we have all done many times, and it is something that we do in part every night when we sleep.

In our sleep, our higher bodies leave our physical body as it rests and experiences an acceleration of the renewal and healing process which is underway whilst we are awake and active in our physical world. Our dreams are a part, and often confused memory, of this process, for we are very active whilst our body sleeps, often in contact with the higher aspects of others also sleeping — friends, family and acquaintances who are incarnated with us, and also those we have known who have already left the physical life.

A client will often feel that they 'met' their deceased father, mother or some other loved one in a dream. 'It was so real,' they exclaim. 'I felt as if they were actually with me.' My reply is usually to tell them that they were with them, and that we recall them as they used to be on the earth, rather than how they are now — in the astral mental worlds, they can appear to us, however we need them to, so that we may recognise who they are.

Those who have died temporarily, as I did when struck by lightning as a boy, are always changed significantly by the experience. There are many researched books on the subject of the near-death experience, but I know, through my own, that we soon discover that our physical body is not who we really are. It is only the temporary outer coating of our personality for this lifetime.

So-called primitive societies often venerate the process of death, and individuals prepare themselves for it. When they are aware of the time approaching, they attend to their affairs, perform any necessary rituals, and then enter the transition into the higher life. They travel through a vortex, often seeming like a tunnel, until they find themselves in another reality, a different place. I remember leaving such a place before birth, as we all do. And it is to one of these 'many mansions' in God's universal 'House' that we return when we have finished our life here.

We should prepare ourselves for death, because, as with any journey, in preparing, we make the transition easier. I remember a famous medium once being questioned by a non-believer about death and the 'spirit world', as mediums often call it. He asked her what she would think if she discovered that she had been wrong all along — that there was nothing after death, and all her messages from the spirits of 'the dead' souls were illusory. She replied, 'Let's look at it this way. If you're right and I'm wrong, I will at least have helped people to cope with the passing on of loved ones; and when we die, you will experience the nothingness you expect, along with me. However, if I'm right and you're wrong, I'll be a little prepared for the next world and you'll wake up to the shock of your life!'

When my great grandmother was a little unwell one weekend, she asked various members of the family to visit her.

During that time, she read the riot act on various outstanding family feuds, made her peace with everyone, and then, a day later, unexpectedly passed on. We all thought that she was suffering from a cold — she knew that she was ready to make her next journey. This is not an uncommon story, and we should all be ready to die, to move on to the next life when the time comes. We have nothing to fear but our fear of death, and a healthy life must include a healthy respect and understanding of dying.

Sometimes, like all healers, I am involved in helping such a transition and, occasionally, those who know and accept their inevitable death ask me to help them to prepare for it. Apart from the obvious privilege it bestows upon the helper, it is a great learning process for which there is no recipe or script. It is a matter of working from the heart, the seat of love, and knowing beyond doubt the essential continuity and imperishable connections of life.

If you would indeed behold the spirit of death, open your heart wide unto the body of life. For life and death are one, even as the river and the sea are one … For what is it to die but to stand naked in the wind and to melt into the sun? And what is it to cease breathing but to free the breath from its restless tides, that it may rise and expand and seek God unencumbered?

The Prophet — Gibran

Our attunement to our soul, through our prayer and meditation life, will prepare us for our transition; for many, it is the ultimate healing.

Approaching Death

~   *If you know someone who is about to pass over, offer them a prayer of blessing and dedication for their journey.*

~   *Be dignified and cheerful in their presence. Your own sense of the eternal is transmitted to them both through your words and in the precious silent moments you may share with them.*

~   *With your inner vision, see the beautiful light in their crown centre, open and clear, allowing them, when they are ready, to make the journey upwards and out through the physical body, their spirit being able to soar away through the light in their head, like a beautiful bird. We do not wish to keep them here when they are ready to move on. We should not wish to stay when our task is done and the universe needs us active elsewhere.*

A Sleeping Beauty

This tale, in various forms, and like all folk-tales, is a spiritual allegory, relating to our soul journey and our ultimate healing. On my courses, clients often find themselves in the role of the Prince, or of the Sleeping Beauty, as they re-enact the divine story. Remember this story for yourselves and the healing it demonstrates.

The Sleeping Beauty lies in suspended animation, poisoned by the wickedness and ignorance of life, personified in the curse of a jealous, envious witch. She can be awakened only by the kiss of a Prince, and so she slumbers for a hundred years, as the weeds, brambles and thistles grow around her in the castle in which she lies.

The story illustrates to us the problems of this world — our separation from the goodness of life as its fear and hatred drag us down, seemingly cutting us off from our joy, our real happiness. We are in suspended animation. Diseased and near dead, we may need a miracle to save us, to heal us, to wake us up to our real power. In our moment of desperation, our soul and spiritual nature do not give up on us but send their messenger. Our extremity really is God's opportunity.

The Prince is the soul's messenger, arriving with his sword of truth to cut away the overgrowth of thorns and debris, which for so long have denied us in our fear and separation. He clears his path, as in our meditation we clear a path through the negative thoughts and ideas of limitation in the lower astral plane. The aspiring Prince, our soul, is then able to awaken us, the Sleeping Beauty, with the kiss of life, the touch of enlightenment, the fusion of soul and personality.

At last, we are truly alive again. We are awakened, enlightened and united with our real self. The mists of separation have dissolved. We are at one. We are whole. We are healed.

CHAPTER 7

HEALING FOR OTHERS

Perhaps our greatest validation as individuals is in what we do in our lives to help others. Our greatness as human beings is not measured by what we take, but in what we give.

Of course, to be an effective therapist for someone else we have to attend to ourselves and our own healing first, and the preceding pages of this book are more than adequate to enable you to work through that process, using the ideas and exercises, assessing where your need is greatest.

However, a significant proportion of my clients are health professionals and therapists of various kinds, some of whom come to me for specific training and development in the practice of energetic methods and approaches to healing. In this chapter we will consider a few particular approaches I use, some suitable for anyone with a compassionate heart, and some, perhaps, more suited to those who already have some experience in the healing arts.

My own training as a healer has been virtually all intuitive. It is my contention that many of the courses currently offered, whilst good in parts, are often taught by people with little more experience and awareness than their pupils. And various attunements and systems are promoted with allusions to exclusivity and uniqueness — claims which are, at best, dubious and, at worst, rather misleading and false.

Anyone with a sound basis in meditation will open their hearts sufficiently to channel vast amounts of energy through their own energy field, which, in turn, will stimulate the energy field of another in a positive and constructive way. What we can't do is heal each other. No healer or therapist ever healed anyone. And if the person is not ready to grow and move on as is necessary in any healing situation, our ministrations are likely to yield little effect, however often we offer ourselves. Some of the finest healers I have seen have never laid a hand on anyone, but radiate and practise remarkable caring.

Physical Healing

In energetic or so-called 'spiritual' healing, there is another paradox which some healers do not fully understand, and it underlines the futility of attempts to measure such therapy in a manner that will prove to the more conventional medical mind that it works. Often, the more evolved healers are along their own path, the less likely they are to stimulate the healing of the physical body of the patient with whom they are working.

As the healer's own vibratory level rises, so does their responsibility, and the mending or fixing of the physical body becomes increasingly irrelevant, and is certainly not a priority. Of course, all healers (and all patients) seek physical healing, and we should all aspire to that ideal as a part of our healing — seeking to be healed at every level of ourselves.

However, high-vibratory healers are more likely to create an environment in which enlightenment, a deepening spiritual awareness and peace are unfolded in their patients, rather than physical healing of the body. Whilst it is true that all healing is from higher to lower, from above to below, and it is generally true to say that we need our physical bodies healed, nonetheless, as we grow spiritually, the significance of such healing diminishes as more profound issues begin to dominate our awareness, and our fear of death wanes.

Healing through Death

As mentioned earlier, high-vibratory healers are often called to help patients in their death process, just as they will help to heal a bad back or to shrink a tumour. There can be no greater service than this, and I have been asked on many occasions to be involved in assisting a transition from this life to the next. I am very aware of the growth and healing I experience when I accompany someone through their last illness.

We will all die, sometime or another, and we should treat it as a journey and not a finale. I recommend that all healers and therapists should familiarise themselves with the work of Dr Raymond Moody, author of the book *Life after Life* and his research into near-death experiences, along with such works as the *Tibetan Book of the Dead*, so that they may understand this aspect of their work more clearly.

Remember, if you are a healer, your own awareness will affect your patient, both in the spoken and unspoken, and thus you can make their passing so much easier and more creative. As healers, we may sometimes be unwilling to see a patient die and make their next journey. As our compassion rises, we wish to heal all the pain we behold, both in the living and the dying, but, in the healer's mind, the highest good for the destiny of the patient must always be paramount.

An educated perception of the aura, particularly the ray distribution, and especially the activity in the crown chakra, will quickly remove any doubt as to the soul's intention and what is going to happen. If it is deemed by the soul to be the right time, nothing done here will change that. So, we must help patients to be ready to move into the light of the higher life and the worlds to come, if that is what is to be, for death itself is often the greatest healing of all.

A Reflection

~   In your practice, consider you own relationship with life and death, and how you prepare yourself for your eternal journey.

~   Reflect upon the cycles of life, especially the way they are seen in the natural world around us, in the flowers, trees and animals. In particular, be conscious of how death and decay are merely changes of state — nothing dies, it merely transmutes into another level of life.

~   Consider how death itself is simply another birth, just as birth into incarnation on the earth is death to another life — a pre-birth existence whose memory is locked deep in your heart.

For life and death are one, even as the river and the seas are one.

The Prophet — Gibran

Love

As human beings, our greatest gift is our ability to love. Yet, in the sometimes shallow and selfish twentieth-century materialism which has, sadly, spilled over into this first decade of the twenty-first century, love seems to be very low on the agenda.

The reason is simple. We are fearful and our fear denies love. So many of us have become selfish, self-centred, too acquisitive and ungrateful. We are now often unwilling to give, joyfully, freely, without condition, as love demands; and sometimes we receive, with suspicion, or indifference and dissatisfaction, that which we are given.

Love is essentially our capacity to give generously of ourselves into life, and also to allow life to give of itself to us. We have to do both. Some people are wonderful givers, but, at the same time, decline help or gifts from others. To me, this is a kind of selfishness and control and is not truly heart-based. We are designed to receive as well as to give, and we have to experience both to be fully functioning individuals.

We also have to be willing to grow and change if we are to experience the power of love, for it takes us totally into the moment, to be in the joy of every experience, whatever that experience may be. Love isn't stagnant — it is the dynamic force of the human heart, which seeks to express God's creative generosity and magical care through our thoughts, words and actions. Frankly, without love, life is meaningless, and we become like empty shells, devoid of any brightness or warmth. When we are loved, we know that we are. It is like electricity, and perhaps we can't describe it; we cannot really explain how it feels. But we know its effect.

That is why our thinking must always be focused in our hearts. To be a healer, you have to be a lover — a lover of life and everything that celebrates that life. You don't have to believe in God or be perfect (yet!) but true lovers are seekers, who look to exploit the good in themselves for others, and to enjoy, with gratitude, that which life seeks to give them.

You begin with yourself. You learn to honour the magnificence in you, the sheer splendour of your own being and the wonder of your human potential. You seek to bless life and those within it, but first you seek to bless yourself and the great investment the universe has made in you. Daily, after meditations, you should contemplate the following, or similar.

From head to toe
My body is filled with love.
From my head to my toes
I have my body working for me.
Love circulates through me from my heart, ever flowing,
Warming and caressing every tissue,
every fibre and cell in my body.

All the organs of my body are working for me.
I am filled with health-giving love.
My body is fed and cleansed beautifully, as the creative breath
of life flows in
me, renewing and restoring.
I thank and bless my body with love.
Taken from *Being Loving…* — Paul Lambillion

After such an affirmation, reflect on the magnificent light and energy that empowers you for this lifetime, pouring from your soul, through your mind and heart, to support your physical home, your body.

Know you not, that you are the temple of God, and that the
spirit of God dwells within you.
I Corinthians 3:16

Seek ways of showing your gratitude by being one of life's lovers — then you will help others on their journey, whatever you do, wherever you are.

Exercise 27 — A Healing Attunement
There are many healing attunements taught. The following is a simple, safe and effective one, which will enable you to help anyone in a contact situation — a friend, member of your family, or client.

1. Find the centre as in Exercise 5.
2. Bring your focus back to your heart-centre vortex for a few moments. Be aware of the unique quality of the forces of your heart and how it is at the centre of your humanity and your divinity. In your heart, the love of the universe becomes tangible. It is the balance between the extremes of

consciousness in the universe — the atom and the stars meet
and exist in you and encounter each other in your heart.

3. Lift your attention gently up from your heart into your head,
linking first with your pituitary gland and brow centre, and
then with your pineal gland and crown centre.

4. With your imagination, see the light as it pours through your
crown centre, touching first the pineal gland, then the pituitary and brow centre, and then downwards to the beautiful
light of the heart. Here, the energy of compassion increases
the power and vibrancy of this light. From your heart you
now radiate the most beautiful forces which will touch and
comfort anyone in your presence, or anyone you place in
your thoughts at that moment.

5. To give contact healing to someone in your presence, have
them sit quietly on an upright chair in front of you. Imagine
them in the centre of their own light as you did for yourself.
When you have done this, move towards them, place your
hands, palm downwards above their shoulders, in their energy
field, probably two or three inches above the physical body.

6. Dedicate your work with the patient to the highest good for
them that they may fulfil their destiny.

7. Be aware of the light and energy becoming active in your
entire body, but especially in the major heart centre and the
secondary heart centres around your etheric body. Be conscious also of the chakras/vortices in your hands — twelve in
all, one on each finger and thumb tip (see Figure 7.1), and one
in the centre of the palm of each hand. Focus on each centre,
one at a time, starting with the right thumb, across each
fingertip in sequence and then to the right palm. Repeat the
same with your left hand, then remember how you are a
centre of ever-flowing light and energy, and unlimited energy
flows through you now, stimulating beautiful reactions in the
energy field of your patient.

Figure 7.1: Location of major hand chakra vortices

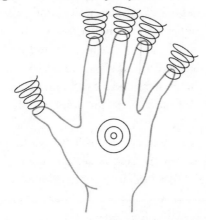

The Unlimited Light of Healing

I would emphasise the word *unlimited*. A mother, who brought her young daughter to see me, sat in on the teenager's session, which is something I always ask with youngsters, or those who are a little nervous.

She was very puzzled later on and telephoned me. Her daughter, who was suffering from post-viral ME, had improved considerably. The cause of her puzzlement was that although she had sat quietly in my office and just observed the session from some feet away, her own chronic spinal condition, about which I knew nothing, had improved considerably, and she was pain-free for the first time for years. The mother was most concerned that she was somehow using up energy that was from the supply intended for her daughter! I assured her that it was not the case, and her daughter's improvement was sustained.

On another occasion, a German client was astounded when, during a workshop where I was demonstrating healing attunements, she experienced a remarkable easing of her own long-term hip problem whilst she observed me working on another participant.

Both cases illustrate two things. First, they demonstrate the expansion and intensity of both the healer's and patient's energy fields during a healing attunement. Secondly, they show how the vast and unlimited nature of the light and energy flow is always more than enough for any situation, and is limited in its impact only by the healer's degree of unfoldment and consciousness and that of the patient, including the karma they are processing at the time.

The healing act in Exercise 27 will have a beautiful effect upon your client or patient, and is actually quite adequate for many situations, and in a healer's early development.

Concluding a Healing Session
~ When you bring your healing to a close, gently step back from your client, giving thanks for the healing that has taken place, for, at some level, there will always be healing.
~ Imagine both you and the patient to be in the centre of your own light respectively, gently grounding yourself, and also your patient, mentally, and verbally, if necessary. Encourage the patient to return very slowly from the experience, as it is harmless and gentle, yet also very powerful and deep in its action.

You will know intuitively how long to keep your hands in position. The act of healing requires only a few seconds — in fact, it takes place in a fraction of that. The rest of the time is for both the preparation and readjustment of the healer and the patient. The remarkable thing about this process is that the vibratory rate or frequency of all the bodies of healer and patient is raised, so the healer benefits as much as the patient.

The Healer's Experience

When you have practised Exercise 27, you will become more sensitive to light, to subtle forces and to energies. You may feel their activity via your nervous system, which will, perhaps, give you one of the following signals —

~ A tingling sensation, predominantly in your hands and finger tips.

~ A warmth also in your hands, especially the left one. This is because, for most of us, our polarity is predominantly positive in the right and predominantly negative in the left, so we feel the 'receiving' effect of energy in the left, negative pole of the left hand. A few individuals are different in their polarity, so it can be the other way around.

~ A cool feeling which I always describe as 'warm, cool creaminess!'

~ A rocking sensation at the base of the spine, linked to the kundalini movement which we will look at shortly.

~ The patient's pain in your own body. If you feel this, it means that your attunement is incorrect and you should practise it again.

Try not to analyse these different experiences if they are new to you. They don't describe different energies so much as your response to them. What you sense may vary from person to person, from day to day.

If you have good, subtle vision, you may see the movement of the forces and energies. The patient will experience a deep relaxation and calmness, and maybe a notable healing of some kind. In some cases, because all disease is a constriction of the natural flow of energy and light, patients may experience some additional discomfort in the ensuing few days, but that will pass, and it will never be unbearable for them. This can occur with all energetic and subtle healing — including acupuncture, various forms of hand healing, shiatsu, homoeopathy and reflexology. Such temporary discomfort is a sign that there is some beneficial activity underway. I remember an early patient of mine who suffered from weekly migraine very severely. After his first healing session, he suffered a most awful migraine attack, which laid him low for almost twenty-four hours. At first, he thought that the healing hadn't worked at all and had actually made things worse. In my naïve inexperienced mind, I wondered what I had done wrong! Happily, it proved to be his last migraine and, whilst I was in contact with him over many years, the condition never returned.

Exercise 28 — Chakra Healing
Once you have mastered Exercise 27, you may progress to direct chakra-based healing. All healing, in fact, must work through the chakras or psychic-centre vortices, as all energy and light travels in such a manner. Even the meridians, the lines of light and energy which link the chakras, have a spiral vortex motion. However, we can enhance our effectiveness in healing activity by making a more conscious connection with them.

1. Seat your patient and go through the stages of Exercise 27.
2. Place your right palm approximately eighteen inches above the patient's crown chakra and your left hand slightly to the left of the vortex, continuing with your attunement as you do so. You will feel a connection here at three levels — mental, astral/emotional, etheric/energetic. Allow your hands to move downwards (right hand) and inwards (left hand), until you feel a resistance as if you were touching the edge of a very soft pillow, very slightly resisting your hands.
3. With practice, you will know intuitively when to move your hands to the next chakra. When that time comes, stand

beside your patient with your right hand in front of the brow chakra vortex and your left hand behind their head, linking with the back of the vortex behind the head. Keep your hands as far away from the physical body as you can to start with, again recognising that you are linking with your patient at all levels — mental, astral and energetic, but most important of all, soul — maintaining your link with the flow of light and energy through you. Allow your hands to move slowly and gently inwards until you meet the gentle resistance as before.

4. When you feel ready to move your hands to the next centre at the eyes, move your hands outwards again, away from the body. Always make your movements slowly, gently and quietly.

5. Repeat this process at each major centre, moving down the spinal column — you will dwell at some centres longer than others, as your intuition guides you. When you reach the root centre, use your hands as you did for the crown centre, only this time, with your right hand underneath the centre. Should this prove physically difficult, simply cup both hands underneath the root chakra vortices.

6. When you have completed the process, return to the crown centre, using your hands as you did at the beginning of the process. You will almost certainly notice that a significant change has occurred to the level of resistance of the energy of the vortex, and your hands will sense that. After a few moments, allow your hands to move to rest upon the energy of the shoulders, and then bring the session to a close as before, visualising both yourself and your client, each in the centre of your own light, grounding yourself and your patient through the feet.

Again, as always, the patient should readjust to everyday awareness slowly, and you may have to talk them gently back into their body. If you do so, tell them to imagine their physical body to be a garment that they have removed temporarily, and now they are putting it back on carefully, from top to bottom, finally feeling their feet firmly in their shoes on the floor beneath them.

This latter part is important. Some people will drift into a deep state and take a while to readjust. Others will appear to remain nearer to the surface in normal consciousness. However, in all cases, take it slowly. And some souls, especially in a first healing, may be very sleepy for some time afterwards. Should they be, advise them to be driven home, if possible, or to have a brief sleep before their journey.

Particularly at this time, with the planetary energies in increasing flux, and the strong tides of change in the astral/emotional plane, healing work requires great sensitivity and care. Some patients may undergo many very powerful and sometimes dramatic experiences, and the healer must be prepared for this.

Healing the Part that Hurts
It is never necessary for a healer to touch the physical body of a patient in light and energetic working. Healers often do, and it doesn't create a problem when they do. From a healing point of view, it makes no difference.

However, from a psychological point of view, the patient may like the part that hurts to be touched or at least 'visited', so if you know that there is a problem in a particular area or organ, you can work outwards from the nearest chakra, very gently, and place your hands in the aura, over the relevant location.

Protection
As I have mentioned elsewhere, healers are often taught to protect themselves. Such an idea is ridiculous and misleading, sadly

driven by fear and ignorance. Anyone with even modest clair-voyance will see that such a practice diminishes the flow of energy through the healer's aura and vortex system.

If the healer practises meditation as part of their development and healing, as they surely should, and if they are thoroughly attuned and in the centre of their own light, that is all that is required.

Any healer who needs protection shouldn't be healing.

Couch Healing

In situations where the patient is lying down on a therapy couch or is bedridden, the best method of chakra healing is as follows:

1. Find your centre and attune to your energy flow, as before. Visualise your patient in the centre of their light.
2. With the patient lying on their back, commence by placing your hands, with palms inwards, either side of their head, several inches away. This is the initial contact with their energy field. Then attune to them with your hands above the shoulders.
3. When you are ready, moving your hands gently and slowly as you do, connect with the crown chakra, by keeping the left hand to the side of the head, and the right hand on the edge of the crown vortex.
4. Repeat this at every chakra along the spine down to the base of the spine vortex, with your left palm to the side of the vortex and your right palm facing inwards above it. Again, at each point you will focus on the spiritual, mental, emotional and energetic link you are making, sensing the point of resistance as you allow your right hand to move slowly downwards. As a rule of thumb, it is better to be further away rather than too close to the patient's body. The chakra vortices radiate way beyond the physical body. You will also know intuitively when to move at each stage.

5. To work on the root chakra or centre, stand at the patient's feet and connect with the chakras in the centres at the base of their feet, connecting first with the left foot, then with the right foot.

6. The golden rule with all healing and spiritual activity is to 'leave as you entered', and so, at the conclusion of the session, return to the crown, cupping both hands around the crown-centre vortex, before detaching from the patient as before.

It is perhaps obvious, but allow the patient to sit up slowly when using a couch, lowering it if you can, so that their feet are close to the ground.

The above approach need take only between fifteen and twenty minutes at most, once you have become practised and confident. Give yourself time, be patient, and you will be amazed by how much you can help.

Giving Energy?

A common error amongst healers is to refer to 'giving healing' or 'giving energy'. Whilst driven by good motive, such a statement is a little dangerous since, in such situations, healers can become temporarily depleted if they indeed transmit energy without being properly attuned in the centre of their own light. For an experienced meditator and healer, it is not a problem, as the continuous practice and meditation will ensure an effective flow.

Furthermore, the healer doesn't pour energy into the patient. Not only is it impossible, but it would also be futile, as it would drain away like water from a leaky bucket, as soon as it was done.

The energy and light the healer transmits will work on a radiation basis, and, it is hoped, stimulate the patient's own system into better, more efficient action, wherever that is needed. As a healer, you will get to know where the chakra constrictions are, although it is not necessary to know this to be effective. Diagnosis is often the easy part, and it may take considerable patience and time to discern some improvement in the patient's condition.

Healing is an intelligent process and healing energies and forces know where to go, what to do and the best outcome for the patient.

Joe's Story

Joe had been diagnosed with leukaemia. It was a particularly aggressive form, and the prognosis was very poor.

He had been prescribed Interferon to slow down the progress of the disease, and a friend had suggested he try some healing. He was a very pleasant, straightforward man of fifty-eight who ran his own business and had a fairly uncomplicated view of life. However, he had tended to put his duty to his family before his own desires and had very much worked himself into the ground. Despite his very masculine, physical appearance and outer projection, he was, in fact, quite a sensitive soul. Joe felt things very deeply but didn't always know how to express his feelings. He was no clever wordsmith and used simple language to wrestle with his ideas and emotions, which had been hidden for so long deep inside him.

The leukaemia had pushed him into considering his own condition, his life and the meaning behind it all. He had started to take more time for himself and the things he wished to do. Whilst we should always make service the spur in our lives, we have also to serve ourselves, and it was nurturing time for Joe.

Chakra Breathing

I had noticed in my healing work how I could help in the clearing of a chakra where there were energy constrictions, especially those close to the surface. These were usually the consequence of a shock which had impacted on the patient's energy field some time ago, and were currently being produced or released, or else they were simply coming to the surface naturally in the patient's healing pattern and karmic release.

They are actually visible in all three levels of the chakra vortex — mental, emotional and energetic — but the emphasis is mainly at one level. In cancerous, low-energy disease, it is most likely that they will be seen in the solar plexus, abdomen, and, perhaps, one other centre — being visible at the energetic level of the centre, and probably the emotional level also.

Figure 7.2: Constrictions in chakra

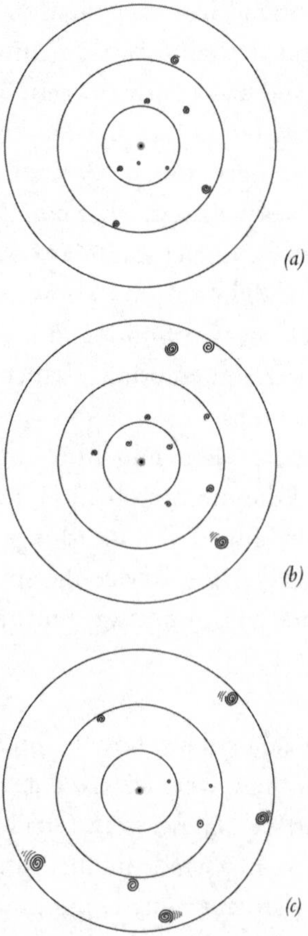

(a)

(b)

(c)

Joe's were very clear in the solar plexus (he also had long-standing, but relatively easily managed diabetes) and the heart centre (common with leukaemia and ailments that are focused in the quality of blood function in the energy/etheric body and astral body).

From an end view of the vortex in a chakra or centre, they can appear like small dots or spots. As they progress nearer and nearer to the surface of the chakra, the constrictions, which are manifestations of thought, emotional substance and the energy attracted to them, reveal their spiral/vortex-like form. (See Figure 7.2.)

They have been held in the relevant chakra, restricting the flow of light and energy at whichever level they are visible, precipitating the manifesting disease. Sometimes, they appear to cling to us, like limpets on the side of a ship, weighing the individual down and impeding progress.

Diagnostic Methods

Everyone has constrictions of this kind somewhere in their system. Our expanding awareness and awakening clears them gradually, at a rate our soul and higher mind deem appropriate. Sometimes, however, like the 'stubborn stains' the advertisements for household cleaners describe, they become stuck, reluctant to move, and the individual repeats the same lessons, over and over again, like a worn faulty record.

Here, the therapist can help the patient with a simple breathing and mental technique that has its roots in yogic breathing.

To diagnose, these are the main methods:

1 — Clairvoyant Diagnosis
~   Diagnosis is achieved with good clairvoyant vision, either objective (outer) or subjective (inner) work through each centre, seeking the constrictions that are relevant to the healing of the patient at that moment. This is very important

thinking. Remember that all healing is 'in the moment', the precious time when a clear beam of consciousness links both the patient and the healer with eternity and the source of our being, when anything becomes possible.

~ It is best, in my experience, to begin with the solar plexus, as it is always heavily involved in any healing. Then to the heart, the meta heart and throat, the abdomen, base and root centres and then the head centres. With practice, you will quickly see and sense which centres are significant ones for you to focus upon.

~ Make a note on your records. In cases where this technique is particularly useful, you will notice several constrictions in the third (outer) layer of the chakra (see Figure 7.2).

2 — Pendulum Diagnosis

~ Using the 'yes' or 'no' technique with your pendulum, as described in Chapter 4, you can determine which chakras/centres are to be given support by chakra breathing. Skilled practitioners can do this before the patient has arrived, using the patient's name as the connecting link, double-checking when they arrive if necessary.

~ Remember to use statements when working with a pendulum and not to ask questions. Statements such as, 'This chakra will benefit from the application of this healing method', or, 'There are significant constrictions in this centre which chakra breathing may help to release', will be suitable.

3 — Hand Diagnosis

~ When you have made your healing attunement and you are working through the centres one at a time, at each point, pause and focus on the sensations in your left hand. Unless you have reverse polarity, which is quite rare, it will be the correct mode of assessment. If you have the reverse energy

polarity, you will tend to experience the most sensation —
tingling, heat, pressure and so on, in your right hand when
you are healing, rather than the usual left.

~ Place your focus in your left hand and be aware of the fluctuations as you move your hand from centre to centre,
Again, your thought must be in relation to the constrictions
in the chakra and the effectiveness of chakra breathing for
its healing.

~ Where the chakra is especially blocked on its periphery, the
sensation in the chakras of your left hand will diminish as
the energy connection is being restricted. It is unlikely that
you will find more than two or three centres you recognise
and are drawn to in this way, and it may well be only one.
Any erratic sensation you may detect in your hands, whilst
you are testing a particular chakra or centre, is a useful indicator that constrictions are near to the surface.

4 — Organic Diagnosis

This diagnosis is simple, yet it is one that I personally do not use,
mainly because of my clairvoyant vision and experienced awareness of energies and forces. However, I have had one or two students who found it an effective diagnostic method.

~ Where there is a specific organic problem, already diagnosed,
find the major chakra or centre vortex closest to it. Usually,
this is easy to do as an exercise in bodily geography.

~ Next, test the centre with your hands, as in the previous
exercise, then test the major centre immediately above and
below to gain a comparative reading as before. Where you
feel little or nothing, that is the centre to work with.

This last method is useful in the early stages of diagnosis as it
gives a starting reference point that is usually readily available to

the healer since there will tend to be a medical diagnosis as its basis.

However, the weakness of it is that the same organic disease in one individual can have a different mix of causes, and therefore chakra roots, from that of another patient.

For example, a spinal condition may have two particular points of manifestation in the spinal column. Links between neck and lower-back problems are common, and one would immediately think of throat and abdomen. In the energy body this would be correct to some extent. None the less, you may well find that the root centre is involved, as it commonly is in spinal problems, along with the solar plexus centre. But since this technique is harmless at worst, and extremely therapeutic at best, no harm can be done in its application — the healer cannot make mistakes as such, but will simply be a little less specific and therefore less efficient. Such a diagnostic method may also preclude the effective removal of constrictions in the emotional body.

Concerning Diagnosis

It is equally important to recognise that the diagnosis the healer makes is not a medical one. It is unwise and un-useful for any healer to make a diagnosis or prognosis at the physical level. The healer's own evolution is unlikely to make that karmically acceptable.

These exercises allow the healer to make a deeper, more active contact with the patient's healing process and, perhaps, help them a little more.

As the possibility of disease always appears in the subtle bodies of the aura and chakras before it manifests in the physical body, it also offers the healer the chance to work with the client at a preventative level as well as a remedial one. That is a wonderful truth that healers should cherish, since constrictions appear in the higher bodies before manifesting in the physical.

Exercise 29 — Chakra Breathing and Healing
Once you have made your diagnosis, and have made and re-affirmed your healing attunements, progress through chakra/centre healing as before. Then, where you link with a chakra which you have selected for this process, work as follows:

1. Breathe rhythmically for a few moments. With well-developed healing attunement, this should happen naturally.
2. Focus upon the chakra, preferably from behind the patient. Take a deep breath and, as you exhale, breathe slowly through your lips and gently into the centre of the chakra vortex. Your head and mouth should be in the mental body of the auric field for the first breath, as level to the chakra as possible. To a certain extent, as you link mentally with the chakra, it comes to 'meet' you, so if you cannot get into a position which is exactly opposite the centre, it is not crucial. They are not fixed or rigid, but move to engage with the entity or light/energy field they need to at any given moment. I sometimes describe it as akin to tentacles on an octopus, although perhaps a little less intimidating than that!
3. Take a second deep breath, this time focusing on the astral level of the chakra vortex, as you exhale through your lips into its centre. Be aware that you are exhaling light and energy, to assist the clearing of your patient's chakra system.
4. The third breath is focused in the etheric/energy level of the chakra and your mouth will be a little closer as you exhale, on the edge of the etheric body, again level with the chakra's spinal position.

When you have done this you can progress with your healing in the normal way, as in Exercise 28.

Some important points with this process are:

~   It is better to work through the back of the patient and
    chakras rather than the front, but either is possible and
    effective.
~   It is unlikely that you will use it on every patient. You will
    know intuitively when to do so, and should tell the patient
    that you are using the technique.
~   Your 'out breath' should always be gentle and slow, as it is
    directed into the chakra or centre vortex — the slower the
    better, as the chakra responds more to a slow, light energy
    stimulus of that kind.
~   Obviously, keep your breath sweet! A pot of garlic or a bowl
    of onions is not ideal before a healing or therapy session of
    any kind and especially when using this technique.

I have found that I use this approach with different clients at
different times. You will not, as one student suggested, spray
germs into their aura! You are channelling energy and virus flow
in and out of your body continuously, mostly harmlessly. Here
you are focusing energy and light, and that is what happens. The
energy and light you channel does not penetrate the chakra
vortex deeply. It has an effect akin to washing the surface of the
centres' layers — it's a little like giving an energy bath.

Joe responded to this approach very well indeed, and I used
it with him often. Doctors were frankly astounded at how well
he responded. He was able to reduce his use of drugs almost
completely, and he also defied the prognosis, puzzling his supervising consultant. Three years on, he was fit and very well and
still running his business, but also living his life more fully than
before in many other directions.

The Cranium

During the past few years of my work, I have witnessed a vast expansion in the practice of many holistic therapies and healing techniques, many of which are very useful. Amongst these, the development of what is termed cranio-sacral work and other specifically head-based healing disciplines is very interesting and significant.

As the expansion of human consciousness gathers pace, certain changes are occurring in us, and the emergence of these therapeutic approaches in particular illustrates remarkably this evolutionary pattern and its effects.

There are three main reasons or causes underlying this movement.

1. *Pineal Expansion* — The first reason or cause is the developing significance of the pineal gland, as mentioned earlier. This most important of glands, now becoming highly active, requires a re-alignment or re-shaping of the cranium in which it resides and by which it is protected. In its awakening, it is seeking to stimulate new areas of the brain that have hitherto remained dormant, so that we may safely access more of the information the pineal gland is filtering for us, flowing in from the universe. This is causing an energetic and light congestion in the head. This congestion, coupled with the misalignments in the cranium, which are the consequence of shocks, tensions, trauma and knocks from our everyday experience, can cause difficulties for us all. Sometimes, birth trauma is also locked in the system and may well find its way to the cranium, or to the sacrum. However, the main problem is our expansion of consciousness and the number of electrical, magnetic and other waveforms to which we are exposed; around our heads we are suffering overload. Our

heads really need to be physically bigger than they are currently, as the energetic pressure increases inside the cranium.

2. *The Three Kundalini and the Rod of Caduceus* — Another reason for our difficulty is found in another phenomenon crucial in our awakening process. It is usually referred to as the three fires, or the three kundalini. Kundalini is a Sanskrit yogic term, alluding to the coiled serpent, supposedly dormant in the base of the spine. In the west, it is the rod or force of Caduceus of Hermeticism and Alchemy, the dragon or serpent slain by St George or St Michael with their swords. This symbol was, of course, later adopted by medicine as a convenient logo, and is still used today. This fire and its spiral movement along the spinal column, weaving its way around and through the major chakra vortices as it travels, is thought to re-unite earthly man with his divine nature in his head, and it rises up with increasing force in proportion to the degree of our awakening. When this force snakes its way up along the spine completely, we are fully awakened. We are most often taught of one movement, from bottom to top, because of our general level of awareness and its predominantly physical or etheric energy-based nature. Most of us do not see or have active perception beyond the material three-dimensional world. That is changing and, as these changes quicken, so we become conscious of other kundalini movements. Sri Aurobindo in his writings on yogic practice explains that the movement and awakening of our awareness of the kundalini power is felt as a descending and an ascending current. My own vision has revealed not only a descending and ascending pattern of spiritual fire, but also a third force which links through a space near to the solar plexus. The three fires or kundalini are:

~ *the physical matter and energetic fire* entering man's system in the root of the spine

~ *the mental and solar fire* linking via the solar plexus and throat chakras

~ *the spiritual and electric fire* which enters via the crown chakra.

The purpose of these fires is firstly for them to blend together so that the spirit in man can operate in the material world through the agency of the mind; and secondly that the physical and energetic man may rise up and surrender to his spiritual source by higher thoughts and understanding. These fires are, in fact, forces that bring to us warmth and energy and ultimately light — light being understanding. When the fires blend in us with increasing efficiency, we become more open, aware and flexible. Cellular change and processes in the body are accelerated, and we heal more quickly and deeply. Our tissues are filled with light. This light-blending illumines and enlightens as it establishes the light of the spirit in the head. Throughout the universe, the blending of fires is the basis of all consciousness and all life, and our three fires are a wonderful example of another universal principle active in us. When these fires are out of synchronisation, we suffer diseases of many kinds, dependent upon the level at which dysfunction occurs.

3. *Shock Transference* — When we are shocked or deeply reactive to an experience, it will impact usually close to the solar plexus. This centre is a major clearing house for personality experiences in the energy, emotional and concrete mental levels. In most of us, the solar plexus becomes overloaded and it discharges the shock along the kundalini or fire movements, up or down the channels around the spine (see Figure 7.3) to the energy fields around the head and the sacrum. The consequence is congestion in the neck and cranial plates and in the sacrum areas.

Figure 7.3: Shock transference along spine

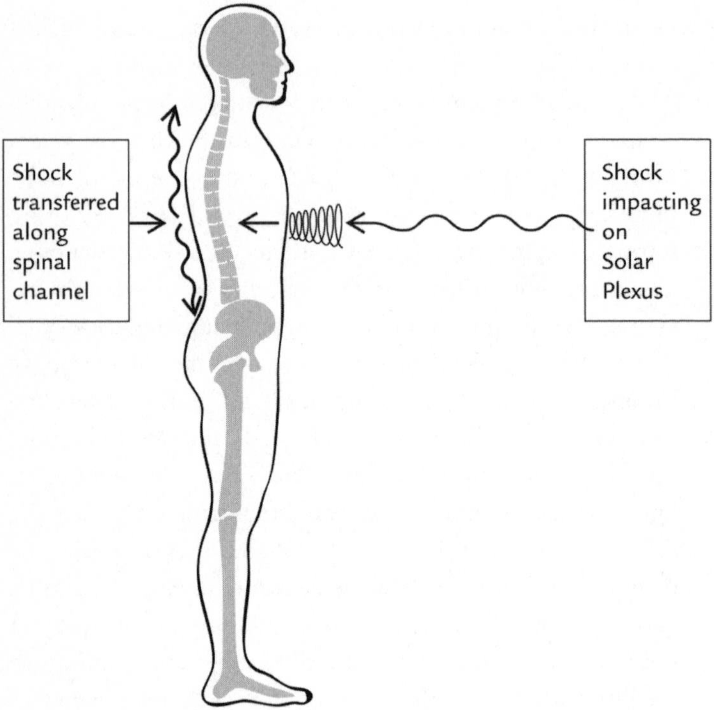

Cranial Healing and Blending of the Three Fires

To be healthy, we must attend to these issues, safely and sensibly, and seek to have balance in the relationship between these fires while, at the same time, encouraging the expansion of the cranial energy field so that we can cope with the increased light we have to process, as heaven (the spirit) and earth (the personality) meet with the skull.

Awareness of the Five Cranial Energy Fields and Plates

The physical head is supported by five major energy plates or fields (see Figure 7.4). These fields govern the shape and balance of the skull, and consequently the function of everything within it. As stress and shock impact through the energy system, the plates become stuck and jammed together, losing the natural pulsing rhythm they normally exhibit, creating pressure in the head. This can also impact upon the astral or emotional body, precipitating anxiety and depression, migraines, feelings of un-reality or being 'spaced out', sleeplessness and tensions in the throat and chest, leading to heart problems, hypertension and asthma. In extreme cases, fitting and epilepsy can also manifest.

Figure 7.4: The five cranial fields or plates

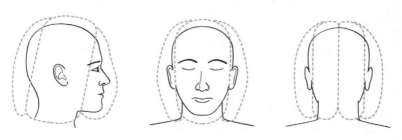

To Develop Awareness of the Cranial Energy Fields

1. Have your subject seated in front of you.
2. Find your centre as before.
3. Make your healing attunement, with particular attention to the sensitivity of six chakras in each hand.
4. *Adhesion* — Place your hands, palms inwards, either side of the head, in the space of the mental body. After a few moments you will feel a connection with the two large energy fields, as a mild sense of adhesion affects your finger-tips and the palm of your hand.
5. *Pulsing and Movement* — As you relax more and more into the process, you will begin to detect a pulsing sensation in

267

the plates of energy. This will be very magnetic, and you will feel your hands being drawn inwards, towards the skull. Go with this a little, but ensure that you keep your hands at least at the edge of the energy or etheric body, in the energy strands — usually at a minimum of three inches apart. This pulsing, which is the rhythm of the blending taking place in the three fires, is very subtle and may take some time to attune to, so be patient. The rhythm of the pulses is in threes, but the tendency of the healer's brain will be to read it as one pulse. The effect is actually as below:

- 1 major pulse   pause

or

1 -> 2 -> 3 minor beats   pause

complete sequence

It is a rising pulse of three minor beats, which feel like small waves, combining as one major pulse, with a pause before the next one commences. This rhythm has a direct correlation to the pulses of the brain.

6. Once you have attuned to this rhythm, allow your hands to move gently outwards, in sequence with the pulsing of rhythm. Keep in your mind that the energy fields know how to move and you are helping to release them. The plates will actually guide your hands, so avoid any sense of manipulation. You are connecting with the natural expansion and re-alignment of the cranium, so be gentle and patient. It is a very subtle movement you seek to connect with. You may sometimes feel your hands turning a little as the pattern unfolds and, after a few minutes, you will have done everything necessary, so gently 'detach' your hands by moving them slowly outwards away from the skull until all sensation has ceased.

7.   Next, repeat the exercise with the two cranial plates at the back of the head. This time, start with your right hand on the right plate, and work simultaneously with your left hand on the left plate. Again allow both hands to attach to the plates and work as before, moving your hands slowly outwards as earlier. After a few minutes when the sequence is completed, detach slowly with each hand.

8.   With the large plate at the front of the head, work firstly with your right hand at the front, and your left hand over the two plates at the back. After a minute or two, reverse your hands, with your left hand to the front and your right at the back. Make all movements of your hands slow and gentle, detaching carefully before re-connecting with the plates.

9.   To conclude the entire sequence, return your hands to the side plates before detaching completely. It is important to remember that this is a very subtle process. It takes patience and is really useful only when some basic attunements have been practised and become properly integrated into the healer's *modus operandi*. Until then, this is best left alone. However, when you do make these connections and become sensitive to the pulses of the cranial fields and the kundalini rhythms, the sense of privilege and wonder at being involved in such a process is beyond describing. And you will be able to help your patients very significantly. The above sequence, if worked on its own, can then be followed by chakra healing from the throat chakra vortex downwards, as in Exercise 28. To derive the greatest benefit for the patient, we then need to attune to the three fires in the following way.

10.   When you have worked with the cranial plates, take your hands to the solar plexus centre, with your right hand one side of the body, left hand on the other, working inwards gently from the mental body level of the chakra (fifth

dimensional), astral/emotional level of the chakra, (fourth dimensional) and finally resting in the etheric/energy level of the chakra (third dimensional).

11. As you do so, be conscious of the balancing activity in the mental fire as it pulses into the space around the solar plexus centre.

12. Next, move your hands to the base of the spine centre. Place your hands either side, again attuning to the kundalini pulsing as you do so. Keep your focus here for some minutes, being guided by the intelligence of that energy as to how long to be connected with it. Intermittently, re-affirm your healing attunement.

13. Slowly, lift your hands upwards to the solar plexus, being aware that you are assisting in the natural blending of the patient's physical and mental energies, their physical and mental fires.

14. After a few moments, lift your hands upwards to the throat centre, linking with the higher mental aspect of the mental fire in your patient.

15. Finally, bring your hands to the sides of the head. Pause for a few moments. You will notice a considerable difference in the pulsing of the energy plates. Slowly, detach your hands. Say your prayer of thanks for the involvement you have had and the integration taking place in your patient. Find the centre for yourself and then for your patient, grounding both of you as your healing draws to a close.

Ingrid

Ingrid was attending a weekend course of mine in Frankfurt. She had come to the city the day before, to visit a local healer who had trained her and helped her considerably.

Ingrid was experiencing some difficulties. She was dizzy, disorientated, anxious and in a state of near collapse. She was brought to where I hold my clinics in the city and I was able to see a significant irregularity in the movement of her kundalini fires. I couldn't determine what had caused this to happen. Ingrid was very distressed and had requested healing help.

I worked through the cranial healing and kundalini process. At one point, she began to spasm, arching her back as if she was fitting, but the subsequent release in her was remarkable. Gradually, she calmed down, perspiring profusely as she did so. She was able to get up, have a cup of tea with me and go back to her accommodation to prepare for the next day's course, which she thoroughly enjoyed.

It was a remarkable healing, and the exchange between the three kundalini was greatly improved. As the movement along Ingrid's spine integrated, the central light channel was perfectly open around her spinal column, enabling a better link between her body, mind, soul and spirit.

This technique can be used intermittently, perhaps weekly, until conditions have improved. In my view, it should be used on everyone periodically in these times.

★

I teach these approaches to students regularly and they are perfectly safe to use if you follow the pattern laid down in this book. They will greatly enhance the work and effectiveness of any healer or therapist who persists and works with an open heart and a clear mind.

In these changing times, you can achieve great things in your healing, both in yourself and with others.

Develop a big-hearted approach to life, to yourself and to everything around you. Then you will heal and be healed, whatever comes your way.

Remember your unique nature, your specialness and how the universe will always support you as you make your journey from disease into ease.

BIBLIOGRAPHY

The following books may be of interest to the reader, in as much as they contain information and ideas corroborating the experience and observations of the author. Whilst the underlying philosophies may be the same, the author does not necessarily endorse their entire contents.

Aurobindo, Sri, *The Synthesis of Yoga,* Sri Aurobindo Trust, 1976.

Bach, Dr Edward, *Collected Writings,* Ashgrove Publishing, 1999.

Bailey, Alice, *Esoteric Healing,* Lucis Trust, 1953.

Barnard, J. & M., *The Healing Herbs of Edward Bach,* Ashgrove Publishing, 1988.

Being Loving is Being Healthy, L N Fowler, 1987.

Bloomfield, Cain etc., *T M,* Unwin paperbacks, 1976.

Braden, Greg, *Awakening to Zero Point,* Radiostore Books, 1993.

Brotherhood of the White Temple Doreal, *The Emerald Tablets of Thoth,* 1939, Source Books 1996.

Capra, Fritjof, *The Tao of Physics,* Fontana, 1976.

Esoteric Psychology, Lucis Trust, 1936.

Holmes, Ernest, *The Science of Mind,* Dodd Mead & Co.

Humphreys, Christmas, *Meditation & Concentration,* Element Books.

Lambillion, Paul, *Auras & Colours,* Gateway/Gill & Macmillan, 2001.

Moody, Dr R. A., *Life After Life,* Mockingbird Books, 1975.

Bibliography

Nils-Axel, Morner, *New Approaches in Geomagnetism and the Earth's Rotation*, University of Stockholm, Sweden, 1988.

Packard, V., *The Hidden Persuaders,* Harmondsworth, 1991.

Ramacharaka, Yogi, *The Science of Breath,* L N Fowler 1960.

Rifat, Tim, *Remote Viewing,* Century Books, 1991.

INDEX

275

AUTHOR'S DETAILS

Paul Lambillion has a range of self-help and teaching cassettes and Flower Chromatic Essences which are available by mail order. He also gives consultations, seminars and workshops in the UK and overseas.

Full details and information on all aspects of Paul's work may be found at:

www.paullambillion.dial.pipex.com

and *www.heartwayusa.com*

or you can email him direct at:

paullambillion@dial.pipex.com.

AURAS AND COLOURS
A Guide to Working with Subtle Energies

PAUL LAMBILLION

Some people are gifted with the ability to see auras, the coloured energy sheath we all have around our physical bodies. An aura reveals an individual's spiritual, mental, emotional and physical state; their personality, gifts, aptitudes and other personal characteristics. Even inanimate objects have auras, as do animals, flowers, trees, houses, communities and cities.

Paul Lambillion teaches people how to discern auras and use this gift in a constructive way so that they can become more effective people and better healers. In this unique book, *Auras and Colours,* he presents a course in learning to understand our subtle bodies, which can bring a deep perception of the whole human being. It includes many useful exercises and meditations, helping us to unfold our own vision of colours and auras.

In addition, the author gives much information on the meanings of the colours and how an understanding of them can bring harmony to our everyday lives.

'With clear illustrations, useful exercises and easy writing style, Paul Lambillion presents a course in learning to understand our energy bodies, which can bring harmony to our everyday lives.'

Psychic News

ISBN: 0 7171 3232 3

From all good bookshops or directly from
www.gillmacmillan.ie